WEEKLY READER PUBLISHING

DAILY LANGUAGE PRACTICE

by Sandy Pobst

Daily Language Practice provides a structured approach to building and reviewing your students' language and literacy skills. Each of the 36 weeks includes daily, weekly, and monthly activities.

Weekly Skill
Practice one skill each week

Monthly Review
Apply skills learned each month

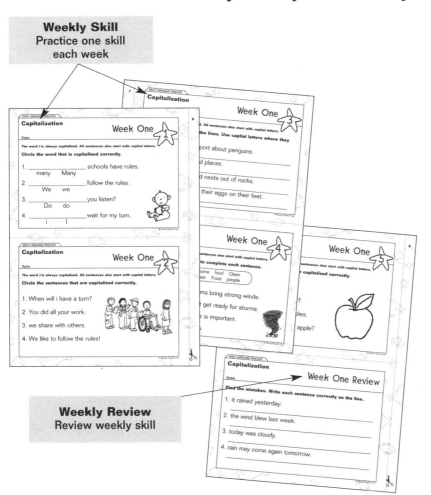

Weekly Review
Review weekly skill

1 2 3 4 5 / 10 09 08 07 06

Table of Contents

Skills: Scope and Sequence

The Scope and Sequence chart on this page provides a complete overview of the skills reviewed in this book. Use this chart to select practice activities that cover skills you are currently teaching or to review previously taught skills.

Skill	Wk 1	Wk 2	Wk 3	Wk 4	Wk 5	Wk 6	Wk 7	Wk 8	Wk 9	Wk 10	Wk 11	Wk 12	Wk 13	Wk 14	Wk 15	Wk 16	Wk 17	Wk 18	Wk 19	Wk 20	Wk 21	Wk 22	Wk 23	Wk 24	Wk 25	Wk 26	Wk 27	Wk 28	Wk 29	Wk 30	Wk 31	Wk 32	Wk 33	Wk 34	Wk 35	Wk 36
Capitalization																																				
Beginning of sentence	X																																X			
Pronoun I	X																																			
Names and titles of people			X																														X			
Names of places			X																														X			
Days, months, and holidays									X																								X			
Titles of books, magazines													X																				X			
Greetings and closings (friendly letters)																															X					
Punctuation																																				
Correct end punctuation	X																																	X		
Periods after abbreviations and titles								X																										X		
Commas in a series										X																								X		
Commas in dates and addresses				X																														X		
Commas in greetings and closings																															X			X		
Apostrophes in contractions					X																													X		
Apostrophes in possessives																					X													X		
Grammar & Usage																																				
Identifying nouns		X																														X				
Singular and plural nouns						X																										X				
Identifying verbs													X																			X				
Action verbs															X																	X				
Forms of be															X																	X				
Identifying and using pronouns																	X															X				
Possessive pronouns																					X															
Contractions							X																													
Identifying adjectives																												X								
Word order											X																									
Complete sentences														X																						
Subject-verb agreement																							X													
Verb tense (past, present)																									X											
Synonyms/antonyms/homophones																								X												
Spelling																																				
CVC and CVCe patterns												X															X									X
Single-syllable with blends																				X							X									X
Final –ck, sight words																				X							X									X
Reading, Vocabulary, & Word Study																																				
Rhyming words																	X																			
Word families																	X																			
Compound words																													X							
Identifying title/author																														X						
Categorizing																			X																	
Real/make-believe																		X																		
Reading graphs, charts, and diagrams																															X					
Inquiry/research																																				
Using parts of a book to locate info																														X						
Alphabetical order																					X															

Using This Book

Daily Practice

This reproducible book provides daily language practice with many essential first-grade language arts skills. You can use these quick activities in a variety of classroom situations—as daily warm-ups, quick assessment tools, or helpful reviews.

The book's organization features 36 weekly practice sessions centered around a single topic, followed by a monthly review of the skills covered during the previous four weeks. This approach allows for in-depth and focused practice of essential language arts concepts in a concentrated time frame. Whenever appropriate, the exercises use material from *Weekly Reader®* magazine. This engaging resource provides high-interest content and skill practice in context.

The exercises offered for the first part of each week are simpler. These afford students the opportunity to experience success while practicing previously introduced skills. As the week progresses, the activities gradually become more challenging. Likewise, the more complex skills are offered as the year progresses.

When planning your daily routine, try one or more of these management techniques:

- Distribute copies of each daily page to individual students or to small groups. You might choose to have students work together for Day One through Day Three and then individually for Days Four and Five. When students work independently, encourage them to exchange work with a partner and compare and discuss their answers. Or, review the correct responses together as a large group.

- Use an overhead projector or create transparencies to complete the work in a large group. Ask volunteers to help complete each item. Try completing Day One as a whole-class activity to review the week's skill. Then have students work independently or in pairs throughout the week.

- Direct students to complete the activity pages for homework. Encourage students to discuss their work with their families.

Weekly Reviews

There is a weekly review to reinforce the work of the previous days. Many of the weekly reviews use a "Find the Mistakes" format that allows students to practice identifying errors in context. You can use this review as an assessment, collecting and scoring each student's work individually. You might prefer to use this skills review as an assessment tool to determine weak areas or gaps in your students' knowledge.

Monthly Reviews

At the end of each four-week set, there is an activity page that reviews the skills taught during that month. Each monthly review includes a "Find the Mistakes" activity or a fun word game.

Skills Overview

The Scope and Sequence chart on the previous page provides a complete overview of the skills reviewed in this book. Use this chart to select practice activities that cover skills you are currently teaching or to review previously taught skills.

Capitalization

Week One

1

Name _____

The word *I* is always capitalized. All sentences also start with capital letters.

Circle the word that is capitalized correctly.

1. _____ schools have rules.
   many   Many

2. _____ follow the rules.
   We   we

3. _____ you listen?
   Do   do

4. _____ wait for my turn.
   i   I

Capitalization

Week One

2

Name _____

The word *I* is always capitalized. All sentences also start with capital letters.

Circle the sentences that are capitalized correctly.

1. When will i have a turn?

2. You did all your work.

3. we share with others.

4. We like to follow the rules!

Capitalization

Week One 3

Name _____

The word *I* is always capitalized. All sentences also start with capital letters.

Write each sentence on the lines. Use capital letters where they are needed.

1. liz and i wrote a report about penguins.

_____

2. penguins live in cold places.

_____

3. some penguins build nests out of rocks.

_____

4. other penguins hold their eggs on their feet.

_____

Capitalization

Week One 4

Name _____

The word *I* is always capitalized. All sentences also start with capital letters.

Choose a word from the box to complete each sentence.

> People   some   food   Clean
> Some   clean   Food   people

1. _____ storms bring strong winds.

2. _____ must get ready for storms.

3. _____ water is important.

4. _____ is important too.

DAILY LANGUAGE PRACTICE

Capitalization

Week One

5

Name

The word *I* is always capitalized. All sentences also start with capital letters.

Circle the sentences that are capitalized correctly.

1. I like apples.
2. May i plant the seeds?
3. Mom and i picked apples.
4. May I taste the green apple?

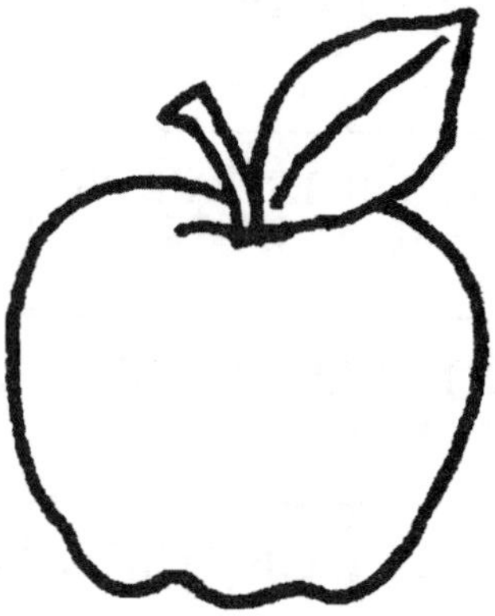

DAILY LANGUAGE PRACTICE

Capitalization

Week One Review

Name

Write each sentence correctly on the line.

1. it rained yesterday.

   ____

2. the wind blew last week.

   ____

3. today was cloudy.

   ____

4. rain may come again tomorrow.

   ____

Punctuation

Week Two 1

Name

Use a period (.) at the end of a statement. Use a question mark (?) at the end of a question.

Complete each sentence. Add a period (.) or question mark (?).

1. Where do you live _____

2. We live in the United States _____

3. Do you know where the president lives _____

4. He lives in the White House _____

Punctuation

Week Two 2

Name

Use a period (.) at the end of a statement. Use a question mark (?) at the end of a question.

Circle the sentences that have the correct punctuation.

1. Have you seen the American flag.

2. It is red, white, and blue?

3. How many stars are on the flag?

4. The stripes are red and white.

Punctuation

Week Two

3

Name

Use a period (.) at the end of a statement. Use a question mark (?) at the end of a question.

Draw a line to the correct end punctuation.

1. What should you do if there is a fire

2. Get out as fast as you can

3. Crawl on the floor if you see smoke

4. Do you have a smoke alarm

.
?
?
.

Punctuation

Week Two

4

Name

Use a period (.) at the end of a statement. Use a question mark (?) at the end of a question.

Complete each sentence. Add a period (.) or question mark (?).

1. Have you lost a tooth _____

2. I have lost two teeth _____

3. They were the front teeth _____

4. Is your tooth loose _____

Punctuation

Week Two

5

Name

Use a period (.) at the end of a statement. Use a question mark (?) at the end of a question.

Does the sentence need a period or question mark? Circle the correct answer.

1. It is summer

2. It is hot outside

3. May we go swimming

4. Where is the sunscreen

.	?
.	?
.	?
.	?

Punctuation Review

Week Two Review

Name

Write each sentence correctly on the line.

1. There is a big web outside

_____

2. Was the spider yellow.

_____

3. I think it was a banana spider?

_____

4. Do they build big webs

_____

DAILY LANGUAGE PRACTICE

Nouns

Week Three 1

Name

A noun names a person, place, or thing.

Look at each noun in the box. Is it a person, place, or thing? Write the word where it belongs.

school flag Mr. Hill students desk

Person	Place	Thing
______	______	______
______	______	______

DAILY LANGUAGE PRACTICE

Nouns

Week Three 2

Name

A noun names a person, place, or thing.

Look at each set of words. Circle the noun.

1. house tall
2. excited Boston
3. old uncle
4. John alike

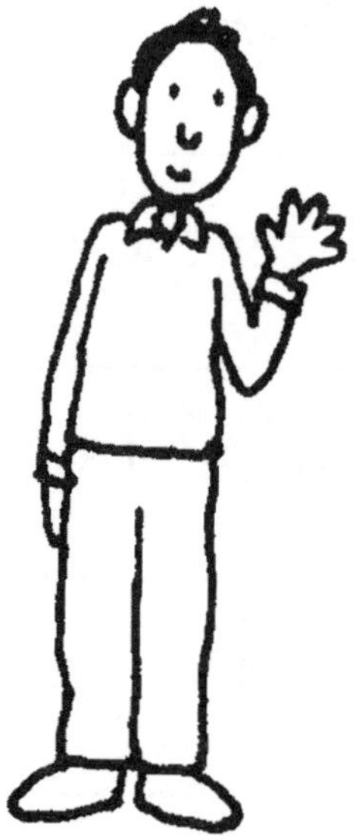

Nouns

Week Three **3**

Name

A noun names a person, place, or thing.

Complete each sentence. Write a noun in each blank.

1. My favorite animal is the _____.

2. I like to eat _____.

3. A _____ lives on a farm.

4. The _____ is a type of flower.

Nouns

Week Three **4**

Name

A noun names a person, place, or thing.

Circle the nouns in each sentence. (There may be more than one!)

1. The children are friends.

2. John reads a book.

3. Seth laughs at a funny story.

4. Soon the boys will go home.

Nouns

Week Three

Name

A noun names a person, place, or thing.

Is the underlined word a noun? Circle Yes or No.

1. We are <u>taking</u> a trip.

2. We will sleep in a <u>tent</u>.

3. I love to look at the <u>stars</u>.

4. They <u>make</u> pictures in the sky.

Yes	No
Yes	No
Yes	No
Yes	No

Nouns

Week Three Review

Name

Circle the nouns in each sentence.

1. Paul likes to play soccer.

2. Ms. Akin teaches us how to play.

3. Carlos kicks the ball.

4. Iris runs down the field.

Capitalization

Week Four

1

Name

People's names and titles start with a capital letter. *Mr.*, *Ms.*, and *Dr.* are titles. Names of places are always capitalized.

Match each word with its name.

1.   friend   Dr. Howell

2.   doctor   Clear Lake

3.   lake   Texas

4.   state   Lee

Capitalization

Week Four

2

Name

People's names and titles start with a capital letter. *Mr.*, *Ms.*, and *Dr.* are titles. Names of places are always capitalized.

Draw a line under the names of people or places.

1. Dr. Martin Luther King Jr. was a great man.

2. He was born in Atlanta.

3. He marched in Montgomery.

4. Many people heard him speak at the Lincoln Memorial.

Capitalization

Week Four

3

Name

People's names and titles start with a capital letter. *Mr., Ms.,* and *Dr.* are titles. Names of places are always capitalized.

Circle the word that is capitalized correctly.

1. The Pilgrims came to _____.

          america   America

2. They did not know how to find _____.

          food   Food

3. The Pilgrims met _____.

     native americans   Native Americans

4. They taught the Pilgrims to plant _____.

          corn   Corn

Capitalization

Week Four

4

Name

People's names and titles start with a capital letter. *Mr., Ms.,* and *Dr.* are titles. Names of places are always capitalized.

Find each name that needs a capital letter.
Write each sentence correctly on the line.

1. Kim and luke play together.

_____

2. bob shares his favorite game.

_____

3. Kate helps william.

_____

4. Joan tells maria a story.

_____

DAILY LANGUAGE PRACTICE

Capitalization

Week Four 5

Name

People's names and titles start with a capital letter. *Mr., Ms.,* and *Dr.* are titles. Names of places are always capitalized.

Look at each word. Write a name that matches.

1. boy ____________________
2. street ____________________
3. girl ____________________
4. city ____________________

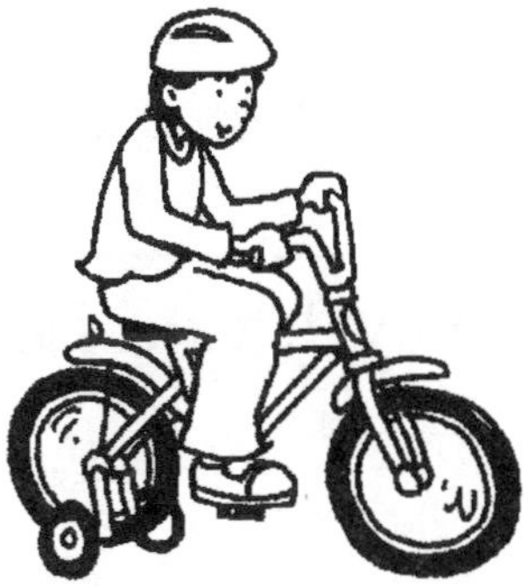

DAILY LANGUAGE PRACTICE

Capitalization

Week Four Review

Name

Write each sentence correctly on the line.

1. My mom walks with me to oak street.

____

2. I am going to see dr. Lopez.

____

3. mr. james calls my name.

____

4. Dr. lopez looks in my ears.

____

Monthly Review

Name

A. Write each sentence correctly on the line.

1. Do you like caterpillars.

_____

2. caterpillars eat plants.

_____

3. We have caterpillars in mrs. krauss's room.

_____

4. My friends and i love caterpillars!

_____

B. Find five nouns. Look across and down. Circle them.

S	B	I	R	D
H	O	M	E	O
F	Y	A	H	G
O	D	V	U	L
D	E	S	K	I

Write the five nouns below.

_____

_____

_____

_____

Commas

Week Five

1

Name

Commas are used in dates and addresses. Commas separate the date from the year: *October 14, 2000.* **Commas separate a city and state:** *Portland, Oregon.*

Are the dates correct? Circle Yes or No.

1. April 1, 1959	Yes	No
2. November 23 2006	Yes	No
3. July, 4 1776	Yes	No
4. December 5, 1957	Yes	No

JANUARY

SUN MON TUE WED THU FRI SAT

Commas

Week Five

2

Name

Commas are used in dates and addresses. Commas separate the date from the year: *October 14, 2000.* **Commas separate a city and state:** *Portland, Oregon.*

Are the cities and states written correctly? Circle Yes or No.

1. Dallas, Texas	Yes	No
2. Denver Colorado,	Yes	No
3. Topeka, Kansas	Yes	No
4. Albany, New, York	Yes	No

Commas

Week Five

3

Name

Commas are used in dates and addresses. Commas separate the date from the year: *October 14, 2000.* **Commas separate a city and state:** *Portland, Oregon.*

Add commas where they are needed.

1. April 17 1995

2. Jackson Mississippi

3. May 22 1933

4. Los Angeles California

Commas

Week Five

4

Name

Commas are used in dates and addresses. Commas separate the date from the year: *October 14, 2000.* **Commas separate a city and state:** *Portland, Oregon.*

Are the commas in the right place? Circle Yes or No.

	Yes	No
1. Our class field trip was November, 2 2005.	Yes	No
2. We went to Cripple Creek, Colorado.	Yes	No
3. Gold was found there on September 9, 1891.	Yes	No
4. We got to look for gold in Victor Colorado.	Yes	No

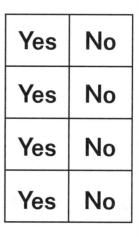

Commas

Name

Commas are used in dates and addresses. Commas separate the date from the year: *October 14, 2000.* Commas separate a city and state: *Portland, Oregon.*

Add commas where they are needed.

1. Fairbanks Alaska

2. February 12 1984

3. June 27 2006

4. Akron Ohio

Commas

Name

Write each sentence correctly on the line.

1. We waved the flag on July 4 2006.

   _____

2. We had a picnic in Elk Falls Kansas.

   _____

3. Thanksgiving is November 23 2006.

   _____

4. We will go to Nashville Tennessee.

   _____

Contractions

Week Six

1

Name

Contractions are shortened words that combine two words. *Are* and *not* are combined in the contraction *aren't*. Contractions include apostrophes.

Draw a line from each contraction to its two words.

1.   I'm   you will

2.   you'll   here is

3.   didn't   I am

4.   here's   did not

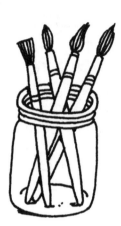

Contractions

Week Six

2

Name

Contractions are shortened words that combine two words. *Are* and *not* are combined in the contraction *aren't*. Contractions include apostrophes.

Draw a line from each set of words to the contraction that matches.

1.   has not   we'll

2.   we will   I've

3.   I have   isn't

4.   is not   hasn't

Contractions

Name

Contractions are shortened words that combine two words. *Are* and *not* are combined in the contraction *aren't*. Contractions include apostrophes.

Circle the contraction in each sentence.

1. Let's go to the zoo.

2. I'd like to see the koalas.

3. Koalas aren't bears.

4. They don't move around much.

Contractions

Name

Contractions are shortened words that combine two words. *Are* and *not* are combined in the contraction *aren't*. Contractions include apostrophes.

These contractions are missing something! Put an apostrophe where it belongs.

1. I <u>wont</u> eat candy.

2. <u>Id</u> rather be healthy!

3. <u>Ill</u> eat good foods.

4. <u>Dont</u> you want to join me?

Contractions

Week Six

5

Name

Contractions are shortened words that combine two words. *Are* and *not* are combined in the contraction *aren't*. Contractions include apostrophes.

Make a contraction using the underlined words. Then write the sentence with the contraction on the line.

1. <u>Here is</u> my wish.

   _____

2. <u>I would</u> like to fly an airplane.

   _____

3. <u>I will</u> fly in the clouds.

   _____

4. <u>They are</u> so fast!

   _____

Contractions

Week Six Review

Name

Write the sentences correctly on the lines.

1. Youd like this book.

   _____

2. I'ts about the rain forest.

   _____

3. Heres a picture of blue frogs.

   _____

4. You would'nt want to touch one!

   _____

Singular and Plural Nouns

Week Seven

1

Name

Dog is a singular noun. A plural noun names more than one person, place, or thing. *Dogs* is a plural noun.

Look at the words in the box. Write each word in the correct space.

webs   eye   moth   homes   leg   bugs

One   **More than One**

_____   _____

_____   _____

_____   _____

Singular and Plural Nouns

Week Seven

2

Name

Dog is a singular noun. A plural noun names more than one person, place, or thing. *Dogs* is a plural noun.

Circle the correct word.

1. **Spider   Spiders**   are interesting animals.

2. Spiders have eight   **leg   legs.**

3. A spider eats many   **bug   bugs.**

4. A mother   **spider   spiders**   lays many eggs.

Singular and Plural Nouns

Week Seven

3

Name

Dog is a singular noun. A plural noun names more than one person, place, or thing. *Dogs* is a plural noun.

Circle the words that mean one thing.

1.   insect   insects

2.   butterfly   butterflies

3.   flower   flowers

4.   grasshoppers   grasshopper

Singular and Plural Nouns

Week Seven

4

Name

Dog is a singular noun. A plural noun names more than one person, place, or thing. Dogs is a plural noun.

These nouns stand for one thing. Add an *s* to make them plural.

1. cow _____

2. snake _____

3. horse _____

4. dolphin _____

Singular and Plural Nouns

Week Seven

Name

Dog is a singular noun. A plural noun names more than one person, place, or thing. *Dogs* is a plural noun.

Circle the plural nouns.

1. I read a book about kangaroos.

2. They have strong legs.

3. The babies are called joeys.

4. They live in pouches.

Singular and Plural Nouns

Week Seven Review

Name

Write each sentence correctly on the line.

1. Rain forest are in danger.

_____

2. Peoples cut down many trees.

_____

3. They build road and farms.

_____

4. That hurts the plants and animal.

_____

Punctuation

Week Eight

1

Name

Abbreviations and people's titles end with a period (.). *Jan.* is the abbreviation for *January. Mr., Mrs., Ms.,* and *Dr.* are abbreviations for titles.

Draw a line from the word to its abbreviation.

1.	Street	Mr.
2.	Mister	Rd.
3.	Road	St.
4.	Doctor	Dr.

Punctuation

Week Eight

2

Name

Abbreviations and people's titles end with a period (.). *Jan.* is the abbreviation for *January. Mr., Mrs., Ms.,* and *Dr.* are abbreviations for titles.

Titles and abbreviations are sometimes used in addresses. Write these addresses correctly on the lines.

1. Ms Sarah Fallen _____

   146 Main St _____

2. Dr Kim Lee _____

   932 Lake Ave _____

Punctuation

Week Eight

3

Name

Abbreviations and people's titles end with a period (.). *Jan.* is the abbreviation for *January. Mr., Mrs., Ms.,* and *Dr.* are abbreviations for titles.

Is each item correct? Circle Yes or No.

1. Jan 14, 2006	**Yes**	**No**
2. Mrs. Rodriguez	**Yes**	**No**
3. 1705 Duval Rd	**Yes**	**No**
4. Dr Sheehan	**Yes**	**No**

Punctuation

Week Eight

4

Name

Abbreviations and people's titles end with a period (.). *Jan.* is the abbreviation for *January. Mr., Mrs., Ms.,* and *Dr.* are abbreviations for titles.

Abbreviate the underlined words. Write the invitation on the lines.

To: <u>Mistress</u> Jane Barnes   **To:** _____

When: <u>Saturday</u>, <u>February</u> 14   **When:** _____

Where: 27 Duke <u>Street</u>   **Where:** _____

What: Valentine's Day Party!

Punctuation

Week Eight

5

Abbreviations and people's titles end with a period (.). *Jan.* is the abbreviation for *January. Mr., Mrs., Ms.,* and *Dr.* are abbreviations for titles.

Draw a line from the word to its abbreviation.

1.   Monday   Nov.

2.   August   Aug.

3.   November   Wed.

4.   Wednesday   Mon.

Punctuation

Week Eight Review

Name

Write the names and addresses correctly on the lines.

1. Dr Jen Tyler

_____

2. 556 Lake Rd

_____

3. Mr Pat Lewis

_____

4. Oct 31

_____

Monthly Review

2

Name

A. Write each sentence correctly on the line.

1. My family went to Sarasota Florida.

_____

2. We stayed with Dr Reyes and her family.

_____

3. We saw sand shells and dolphins.

_____

4. Ive got some beautiful shells.

_____

B. Find six nouns. Go across and down.
   Write the words in the correct place.

D	R	E	S	S	E	S
O	A	V	O	P	Y	N
G	S	A	N	T	W	A
B	U	W	G	O	S	K
C	A	R	S	S	L	E

(**One**)   (**More than One**)

_____   _____

_____   _____

Capitalization

Week Nine **1**

Name

Names of days, months, and holidays are always capitalized. *Friday, June,* and *New Year's Day* are capitalized.

Write each sentence correctly on the line. Capitalize the days of the week.

1. Our class has art on monday.

_____

2. We go to music on tuesday.

_____

3. We have a field trip next thursday.

_____

4. I will be the leader on friday.

_____

Capitalization

Week Nine **2**

Name

Names of days, months, and holidays are always capitalized. *Friday, June,* and *New Year's Day* are capitalized.

Circle the months that are missing capital letters.

1. I plant seeds in april.

2. Flowers bloom in may.

3. Tomatoes grow in june.

4. We pick pumpkins in october.

Capitalization

Week Nine 3

Name

Names of days, months, and holidays are always capitalized. *Friday, June,* and *New Year's Day* are capitalized.

Circle the words that are missing capital letters.

1. It is cold in january.

2. It snowed last monday.

3. We made a snowman on tuesday.

4. I wonder if february will be cold.

Capitalization

Week Nine 4

Name

Names of days, months, and holidays are always capitalized. *Friday, June,* and *New Year's Day* are capitalized.

Circle the correct word or words.

1. Today is an exciting **Day   day** !

2. It is **January   january**   29, 2006.

3. Today is   **chinese new year   Chinese New Year**   .

4. The new year starts on   **sunday   Sunday**   .

Capitalization

Week Nine 5

Name

Names of days, months, and holidays are always capitalized. *Friday, June,* **and** *New Year's Day* **are capitalized.**

Draw a line under the holidays that are missing their capital letters.

1. February 2 is groundhog day.

2. Many people like valentine's day.

3. Do you play tricks on april fool's day?

4. We had a piñata on cinco de mayo.

Capitalization

Week Nine Review

Name

Write each sentence correctly on the line.

1. We celebrate many American Holidays.

_____

2. presidents' day is in February.

_____

3. Memorial Day is the last monday in May.

_____

4. Many people eat turkey on thanksgiving.

_____

Commas

Week Ten

1

Name

Commas separate words in a list.

Which sentence is correct? Put an X by the correct sentence.

1. ___ Milk and yogurt and cheese build strong bones.

___ Milk, yogurt, and cheese build strong bones.

2. ___ Bread, pasta, rice, and cereal are good to eat.

___ Bread and pasta and rice and cereal are good to eat.

3. ___ Candy, cookies, and cake are not good for you.

___ Candy and cookies and cake are not good for you.

Commas

Week Ten

2

Name

Commas separate words in a list.

Combine the sentences. Write the new sentence on the line.

1. Tom plays baseball.
   Tom plays soccer.
   Tom plays basketball.

_____

2. Samantha likes math.
   Samantha likes art.
   Samantha likes reading.

_____

Commas

3

Name

Commas separate words in a list.

**Read each sentence. Are the commas in the right place?
Circle Yes or No.**

1. I like apples, pears, and peaches.	Yes	No
2. Mom likes bananas kiwi, and grapes.	Yes	No
3. Dad likes oranges, plums, and watermelon.	Yes	No
4. Sue likes melon, limes, strawberries, and lemons.	Yes	No

Commas

4

Name

Commas separate words in a list.

Put commas between the things in each sentence.

1. Kim picked up rocks feathers and shells.

2. She put them in boxes cups and buckets.

3. Kim found yellow white and pink rocks.

4. The feathers were brown gray black and blue.

Commas

Week Ten
5

Name

Commas separate words in a list.

Are the commas in the correct place? Circle Yes or No.

1. Fish, and turtles live in ponds.

2. Fish eat spiders, worms, and flies.

3. Turtles like snails, frogs, and plants.

4. Ducks, geese, and squirrels, also visit ponds.

Yes	No
Yes	No
Yes	No
Yes	No

Commas

Week Ten Review

Name

Write each sentence correctly on the line.

1. We eat the roots of carrots onions and beets.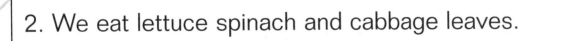

_____

2. We eat lettuce spinach and cabbage leaves.

_____

3. Corn beans and nuts are seeds.

_____

4. We eat the roots leaves and seeds of plants.

_____

Sentences

Week Eleven

1

Name

"I read the book." is a sentence. *"Read the I book."* is not a sentence.

Put the words in order. Write the sentence on the line.

1. pets. Dogs good are

_____

2. They friendly. are

_____

3. like to Dogs play.

_____

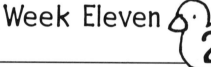

4. petted. to be They like

_____

Sentences

Week Eleven

2

Name

"I read the book." is a sentence. *"Read the I book."* is not a sentence.

Does the sentence make sense? Circle Yes or No.

	Yes	No
1. Life was different long ago.	Yes	No
2. Most room only had schools one.	Yes	No
3. Boys helped with the farm animals.	Yes	No
4. Girls their cook mothers helped.	Yes	No

Sentences

Week Eleven

3

Name

"I read the book." is a sentence. *"Read the I book."* is not a sentence.

Circle the word to complete each sentence.

1. Many kids **water   play** outside.

2. You can stay safe **while   and** you have fun.

3. Never swim by **yourself   alone** .

4. If you ride a **bike   flying** , wear a helmet.

Sentences

Week Eleven

4

Name

"I read the book." is a sentence. *"Read the I book."* is not a sentence.

Does the sentence make sense? Circle Yes or No.

1. There four are seasons each year.	**Yes** **No**
2. May snow ice bring winter and.	**Yes** **No**
3. Most start in fall schools the.	**Yes** **No**
4. Which season is your favorite?	**Yes** **No**

Sentences

Week Eleven
5

Name

"I read the book." is a sentence. *"Read the I book."* is not a sentence.

Circle the word to complete each sentence.

1. Ponds are full of   **life**   **like**   .

2. Frogs and   **fine**   **fish**   live in ponds.

3. **Some**   **So**   do turtles.

4. Some animals   **are**   **for**   too small to see.

Sentences

Week Eleven Review

Name

"I read the book." is a sentence. *"Read the I book."* is not a sentence.

Fix the mistakes. Write each sentence on the line.

1. today. snowed It

   _____

2. coat? is your Where

   _____

3. are mittens? Where your

   _____

4. a Let's snowman! make

   _____

Spelling

Week Twelve

Name

Many words follow a spelling pattern.

Circle the word that is spelled correctly.

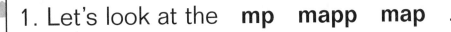

1. Let's look at the **mp   mapp   map** .

2. **Kan   Can   Kin** you find the park?

3. Does the **bus   buss   busy** stop at the school?

4. I do **nott   not   note** see the store.

Spelling

Week Twelve

Name

Many words follow a spelling pattern.

Circle the word that is spelled correctly.

1. This is a body of water.   lak   lake   layk

2. You use this to smell.   noze   nos   nose

3. What your teeth do   bite   bit   byt

4. Baby animals are _____   cut   kute   cute

Spelling

Week Twelve
3

Name

Many words follow a spelling pattern.

Circle the word that is NOT spelled correctly.

1. Birds come to the feeder evry day.

2. They et the seeds.

3. A cat watches thim.

4. The birds fli away.

Spelling

Week Twelve
4

Name

Many words follow a spelling pattern.

Circle the word that is spelled correctly.

1. The opposite of *under*   over   ovr   ohver

2. An animal friend   pit   pat   pet

3. The opposite of *close*   opin   open   opn

4. The number after *four*   five   fiv   fife

Spelling

Week Twelve

Name

Many words follow a spelling pattern.

Circle the word that is spelled correctly.

1. **Brown   Broun   Bron**   bears live in cold places.

2. They often   **livf   liv   live**   near trees.

3. They use their claws to   **dig   dg   digg**   for food.

4. **Sume   Some   Som**   brown bears eat fish.

© Weekly Reader Corp.

Spelling

Week Twelve Review

Name

Write each sentence correctly on the line.

1. Summer can be hott.

_____

2. You need to tak care of your dog.

_____

3. Giv him lots of clean water.

_____

4. Go for a walk wen it is cool.

_____

© Weekly Reader Corp.

Monthly Review

Name _____

A. Write each sentence correctly on the line.

1. We go to the circus on July 8 2006.

   _____

2. We fun have circus. at the

   _____

3. The clown make us laugh.

   _____

4. Sum clowns drive cars.

   _____

B. Find six months. Go across and down. Write them correctly on the lines.

A	U	G	U	S	T	E	M
O	C	T	O	B	E	R	A
S	J	A	N	U	A	R	Y
J	U	L	Y	A	P	R	L
U	N	O	M	A	R	C	H

_____

_____

_____

_____

_____

Capitalization

Week Thirteen 1

Name

Titles of books and magazines are capitalized. Always capitalize the first, last, and any important words. *A, an,* and *the* are not capitalized unless they are the first or last word.

Is the title written correctly? Circle Yes or No.

1. The Way To The Zoo	Yes	No
2. Winter Fun	Yes	No
3. A Song in the Desert	Yes	No
4. In the deep, deep Sea	Yes	No

Capitalization

Week Thirteen 2

Name

Titles of books and magazines are capitalized. Always capitalize the first, last, and any important words. *A, an,* and *the* are not capitalized unless they are the first or last word.

Write each title correctly on the line.

1. the big book of snakes

_____

2. under the sea

_____

3. a letter from home

_____

4. a hat for a hen

_____

Capitalization

Week Thirteen

3

Name _____

Titles of books and magazines are capitalized. Always capitalize the first, last, and any important words. *A, an,* and *the* are not capitalized unless they are the first or last word.

The underlined words are titles. Write each sentence on the line using the correct capital letters.

1. I love to read <u>sheep in a jeep</u>.

   _____

2. Our class likes to read <u>your big backyard</u>.

   _____

3. I like the <u>cat in the hat</u>.

   _____

Capitalization

Week Thirteen

4

Name _____

Titles of books and magazines are capitalized. Always capitalize the first, last, and any important words. *A, an,* and *the* are not capitalized unless they are the first or last word.

Is the title written correctly? Circle Yes or No.

	Yes	No
1. Hattie and the Fox	Yes	No
2. Just Going To the Dentist	Yes	No
3. Sammy The Seal	Yes	No
4. Home for a puppy	Yes	No

Capitalization

Week Thirteen

5

Name _____

Titles of books and magazines are capitalized. Always capitalize the first and last words. _A, an,_ and _the_ are not capitalized unless they are the first or last word.

The underlined words are titles. Write each sentence on the line using correct capital letters.

1. the life of a frog

   _____

2. looking for rainbows

   _____

3. the sky high house

   _____

4. the story of silk

   _____

Capitalization

Week Thirteen Review

Name _____

Write each sentence correctly on the line.

1. My brother likes to read <u>hop on pop</u>.

   _____

2. Have you read <u>Mike And The Bike</u>?

   _____

3. <u>Duck on a bike</u> will make you laugh!

   _____

4. I just read <u>farmer in the dell</u>.

   _____

Verbs

Week Fourteen

1

Name

A verb shows action. *Climb* is a verb.

Look at each set of words. Circle the verb.

1. kick   ball

2. toy   swim

3. blow   sky

4. food   run

Verbs

Week Fourteen

2

Name

A verb shows action. *Climb* is a verb.

Is the underlined word a verb? Circle Yes or No.

1. Friends <u>talk</u> to each other.	Yes	No
2. The clouds are <u>white</u>.	Yes	No
3. We <u>ride</u> our bikes.	Yes	No
4. Sonya and I <u>swim</u> on the team.	Yes	No

Verbs

Week Fourteen 3

Name _____

A verb shows action. *Climb* **is a verb.**

Circle the verb in each sentence.

1. Penguins hunt for food in the ocean.

2. Penguins dive into the cold water.

3. Their feathers keep them warm.

4. Some penguins build nests of rocks.

Verbs

Week Fourteen 4

Name _____

A verb shows action. *Climb* **is a verb.**

Write a verb in each blank.

1. I _____ to stay healthy.

2. The animals _____ in the forest.

3. Kim and Jill _____ after school.

4. I like to _____ with my family.

Verbs

Week Fourteen

5

Name

A verb shows action. *Climb* **is a verb.**

Is the underlined word a verb? Circle Yes or No.

1. Elephants live in <u>hot</u> places.	Yes	No
2. Their big ears <u>keep</u> them cool.	Yes	No
3. Elephants <u>take</u> baths every day.	Yes	No
4. Then <u>they</u> cover their skin with dirt.	Yes	No

Verbs

Week Fourteen Review

Name

Circle the verb in each sentence.

1. Many people eat oranges.

2. Oranges grow in warm places.

3. Oranges turn orange when it is cold.

4. Oranges stay green in hot weather.

Sentences

Week Fifteen
1

Name

A complete sentence has a subject and a verb. *The children rode their bikes.*
The children is the subject; *rode* is the verb.

Is each group of words a sentence? Circle Yes or No.

1. Frog eggs in the water.

Yes	No

2. The tadpole grows legs.

Yes	No

3. The tail shorter.

Yes	No

4. Now it is a frog.

Yes	No

Sentences

Week Fifteen
2

Name

A complete sentence has a subject and a verb. *The children rode their bikes.*
The children is the subject; *rode* is the verb.

These words are not sentences. Add words to make sentences.

1. The tall trees _____.

2. _____ fell to the ground.

3. _____ rake the leaves.

4. It is fun to _____.

5. I love _____!

Sentences

Week Fifteen

3

Name

A complete sentence has a subject and a verb. *The children rode their bikes.*
The children is the subject; *rode* is the verb.

Is each group of words is a sentence? Circle Yes or No.

1. Plants need four things to grow.

2. Air and sunlight.

3. Food for the plant.

4. Plants also need water.

Yes	No
Yes	No
Yes	No
Yes	No

Sentences

Week Fifteen

4

Name

A complete sentence has a subject and a verb. *The children rode their bikes.*
The children is the subject; *rode* is the verb.

These words are not sentences. Add words to make sentences.

1. _____ rolled across the floor.

2. The new blocks _____.

3. My friend and I _____.

4. _____ was tall.

Sentences

Week Fifteen 5

A complete sentence has a subject and a verb. *The children rode their bikes.*
The children is the subject; *rode* is the verb.

Is each group of words a sentence? Circle Yes or No.

1. A newspaper.	**Yes** **No**
2. Newspapers tell us what is happening.	**Yes** **No**
3. Sometimes the stories.	**Yes** **No**
4. Newspapers help us learn about the world.	**Yes** **No**

Sentences

Week Fifteen Review

Match the words to make sentences.

1. My brother   helps him catch the ball.

2. His mitt   practice too.

3. Sometimes it   plays baseball.

4. The other players   is hard to hit the ball.

Pronouns

Week Sixteen

1

Name

Pronouns take the place of nouns. *I, he, she, me, you,* and *it* are pronouns.

Circle the pronoun that fits each sentence.

1. **I**   **Me**   like to skate.

2. **His**   **He**   wants to skate fast!

3. **She**   **Her**   will bring her own skates.

4. **It**   **I**   is cold on the ice.

Pronouns

Week Sixteen

2

Name

Pronouns take the place of nouns. *I, he, she, me, you,* and *it* are pronouns.

Circle the pronoun that fits each sentence.

1. May   **us**   **we**   go to the park?

2. **I**   **It**   is a nice sunny day.

3. Brynn and   **I**   **me**   will ride bikes.

4. **We**   **It**   will all have fun.

Pronouns

Week Sixteen 3

Name

Pronouns take the place of nouns. *I, he, she, me, you,* and *it* are pronouns.

Circle the pronoun that fits each sentence.

1. Mrs. Simmons dropped **it** **she** .

2. Mr. Woods found **they** **them** .

3. Will you go with **I** **me** ?

4. Do you want **we** **us** to help?

Pronouns

Week Sixteen 4

Name

Pronouns take the place of nouns. *I, he, she, me, you,* and *it* are pronouns.

Circle the pronouns in each sentence.

I	he	she	it	we	they
you	me	him	her	us	them

1. Will you sing me a song?

2. They like me.

3. She and I run races.

4. Can he go with us?

Pronouns

Week Sixteen

5

Pronouns take the place of nouns. *I, he, she, me, you,* and *it* are pronouns.

Choose a pronoun from the box to complete each sentence. Write it in the blank.

1. John read a book.

   _____ read a book.

   John read _____.

2. The cat followed Bill home.

   _____ followed Bill home.

   The cat followed _____ home.

it	He
him	She

Pronouns

Week Sixteen Review

Write each sentence correctly on the line.

1. Julia and me went to the movies.

   _____

2. Them are friends.

   _____

3. Her likes to write.

   _____

4. Him and Cheryl are in the story.

   _____

Monthly Review

Name

Put an X next to the sentence with a verb that shows action.

1. _____ Kangaroos jump with strong legs. (S)

_____ Kangaroos are brown. (W)

Put an X next to the sentence that is correct.

2. _____ Me and Jimmy went to the zoo. (T)

_____ Jimmy and I went to the zoo. (P)

Put an X next to the sentence that is correct.

3. _____ I read <u>where the Wild Things are</u>. (O)

_____ I read <u>Where the Wild Things Are</u>. (I)

Put an X next to the complete sentence.

4. _____ The brown bear was very tall. (N)

_____ The cute little bear cubs. (S)

Each answer has a letter circled.
Write that letter in the correct circle below.

Why are spiders like tops?

Because they
                  1   2   3   4

Verbs

Week Seventeen

Name

A verb shows action or being. *Climb* is an action verb. *Is, are, was, were,* and *am* are verbs of being.

Circle the verb in each sentence.

1. The eagle flies.

2. The dolphin dives into the water.

3. Ducks waddle away.

4. The monkey swings in the tree.

Verbs

Week Seventeen

Name

A verb shows action or being. *Climb* is an action verb. *Is, are, was, were,* and *am* are verbs of being.

Circle the verb in each sentence.

1. My friends are taller than me.

2. The puppy was cute.

3. I am happy.

4. The kittens were sleepy.

Verbs

Week Seventeen

3

Name

A verb shows action or being. *Climb* is an action verb. *Is, are, was, were,* and *am* are verbs of being.

Circle the verbs in each sentence.

1. Our class wrote a play.

2. I am the queen.

3. Alex is the king.

4. He sings a song.

Verbs

Week Seventeen

4

Name

A verb shows action or being. *Climb* is an action verb. *Is, are, was, were,* and *am* are verbs of being.

Are the underlined words verbs? Circle Yes or No.

1. The raccoon <u>has</u> a mask.	Yes	No
2. The mask <u>is</u> on its face.	Yes	No
3. Raccoons eat <u>fruits</u>.	Yes	No
4. They <u>are</u> fun to watch.	Yes	No

DAILY LANGUAGE PRACTICE

Verbs

Week Seventeen 5

Name

A verb shows action or being. *Climb* is an action verb. *Is, are, was, were,* and *am* are verbs of being.

Draw a line under the verbs.

1. A beaver builds a home.
2. It uses mud and sticks.
3. The home is near the water.
4. Beavers are good swimmers.

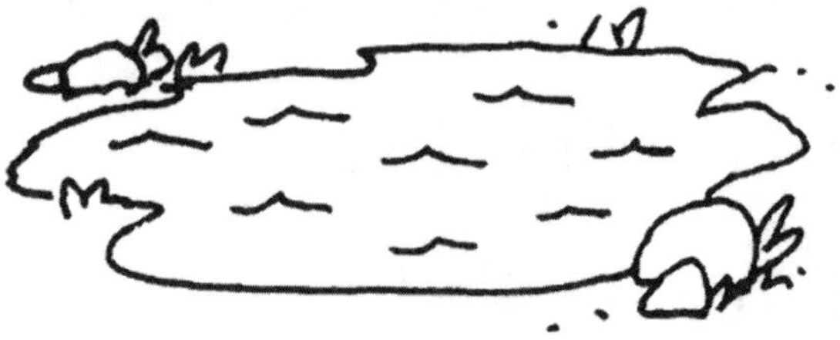

DAILY LANGUAGE PRACTICE

Verbs

Week Seventeen Review

Name

A verb shows action or being. *Climb* is an action verb. *Is, are, was, were,* and *am* are verbs of being.

Circle the verbs.

1. Ellen and Sam help at home.
2. They clean their rooms.
3. They hang their clothes up.
4. The children are helpful.

Rhyming Words

Week Eighteen

1

Name

Rhyming words end with the same sound. Sometimes they are spelled alike.

Circle the words that rhyme.

1. feed   frog   seed

2. log   goat   boat

3. jar   star   lug

4. lick   mop   hop

Rhyming Words

Week Eighteen

2

Name

Rhyming words end with the same sound. Sometimes they are spelled alike.

Draw lines to match the words that rhyme.

1. brick   well

2. smell   tall

3. book   stick

4. ball   look

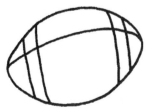

Rhyming Words

Week Eighteen

3

Name _____

Rhyming words end with the same sound. Sometimes they are spelled alike.

Write a word that rhymes.

1. see _____

2. stop _____

3. bed _____

4. car _____

Rhyming Words

Week Eighteen

4

Name _____

Rhyming words end with the same sound. Sometimes they are spelled alike.

Does the word pair rhyme? Circle Yes or No.

1. blow   star

2. hat   mat

3. hug   cow

4. jar   car

Yes	No
Yes	No
Yes	No
Yes	No

DAILY LANGUAGE PRACTICE

Rhyming Words

Week Eighteen 5

Name

Rhyming words end with the same sound. Sometimes they are spelled alike.

Circle the words that rhyme.

1.	chop	map	hop
2.	slip	drop	drip
3.	fall	fill	pill
4.	wall	ball	well

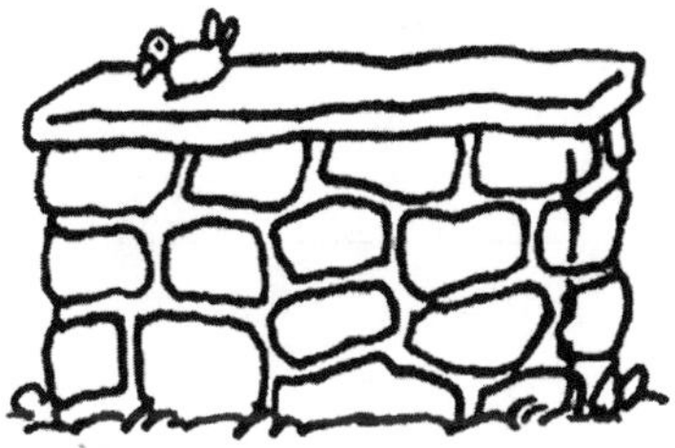

DAILY LANGUAGE PRACTICE

Rhyming Words

Week Eighteen Review

Name

Choose a word from the box that rhymes with the underlined word. Write it on the line.

house sky stink How

1. Why is the ________________ blue?
2. If you think you ________________, take a bath!
3. Does a mouse live in a ________________?
4. ________________ does a cow make milk?

Categorizing

Week Nineteen

1

Name

Sort words into groups or categories. These words have something in common.

Write each word in the correct group.

star   ant   tree   grass   moon   sun

Things in the Sky   **Things on the Ground**

_____   _____

_____   _____

_____   _____

Categorizing

Week Nineteen

2

Name

Sort words into groups or categories. These words have something in common.

Circle the things that fly.

1. birds   fish   snake

2. log   bee   lion

3. hat   car   kite

4. train   sun   plane

Categorizing

Week Nineteen

3

Name

Sort words into groups or categories. These words have something in common.

Can these animals fly? Circle Yes or No.

1. bear	Yes	No
2. cow	Yes	No
3. parrot	Yes	No
4. owl	Yes	No

Categorizing

Week Nineteen

4

Name

Sort words into groups or categories. These words have something in common.

Do these animals have feathers? Write Yes or No.

1. rabbit _____

2. duck _____

3. lizard _____

4. penguin _____

Categorizing

Week Nineteen

5

Name

Sort words into groups or categories. These words have something in common.

Think of a name for each category.

_____   _____

shark   tree

tadpole   flower

whale   grass

turtle   bush

Categorizing

Week Nineteen Review

Name

Circle the mistakes in each list.

Things We Eat   **Living Things**

nuts   cars

apples   people

grass   rocks

cheese   cats

dirt   sunflowers

Spelling

Week Twenty

1

Name

Many words follow a spelling pattern.

Circle the word that is spelled correctly.

1. Opposite of sorry   gad   glad   glid

2. Make a sound with your hands   clap   clam   klap

3. Opposite of bumpy   flatt   flet   flat

4. To break   snap   stap   snp

Spelling

Week Twenty

2

Name

The letter _r_ can change the sound of a vowel.

Circle the word that is spelled correctly.

1. There   **ar**   **are**   12 months in a year.

2. What is   **yor**   **your**   favorite season?

3. I heard a dog   **brk**   **bark**   .

4. A   **bird**   **burd**   has feathers.

Spelling

Week Twenty

3

Name

The –k sound at the end of a word is sometimes spelled with –ck.

Circle the correct word.

1. I heard the bird   **quack**   **quak**   .

2. It was a   **duk**   **duck**   .

3. It swam near a   **rok**   **rock**   .

4. I will   **walk**   **walck**   over and see it.

Spelling

Week Twenty

4

Name

The letter r can change the sound of a vowel.

Write the corrected sentence on the line.

1. I went to the pahrk to play.

   _____

2. It was my tern on the swing.

   _____

3. I fell in the durt.

   _____

4. I hirt my arm.

   _____

Spelling

Week Twenty

5

Name

Some words follow common patterns.

Circle the word that is spelled correctly.

1. Move around in circles   spinn   spen   spin

2. To fall   slip   slep   salip

3. An insect   ant   antt   ante

4. An animal that hops   frag   frog   frogg

Spelling

Week Twenty Review

Name

Write each sentence correctly on the line.

1. Sharcks swim in the ocean.

_____

2. Watch the bird flapp its wings!

_____

3. The chik peeped loudly.

_____

4. The farmer's krop grew fast.

_____

Monthly Review

Name _____

A. Write each sentence correctly on the line.

1. We see many strs at night.

_____

2. The sun are a star too.

_____

3. All stars is made of gases.

_____

4. They are verry hot.

_____

B. Write a word that rhymes with each word below.

1. tall   _____
2. day   _____
3. lock   _____
4. rake   _____

**C. Find four things that have fur. Go across and
   down. Circle them.**

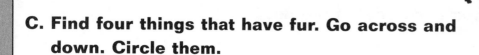

L	L	A	M	A	O
O	B	M	O	N	T
H	E	N	O	T	T
A	E	K	S	C	E
R	S	B	E	A	R

Real and Make-Believe

Week Twenty-One

(1)

Name

Things that are *real* happen. Things that are *make-believe* could not happen.

Is this real? Circle Yes or No.

1. The hats walked down the street.	Yes	No
2. The chicken sang a song.	Yes	No
3. The boy hid behind the tree.	Yes	No
4. Dad sat in his chair.	Yes	No

Real and Make-Believe

Week Twenty-One

(2)

Name

Things that are *real* happen. Things that are *make-believe* could not happen.

Is this make-believe? Circle Yes or No.

1. The bird flew into the air.	Yes	No
2. The penguin danced a jig.	Yes	No
3. The blue jay turned red.	Yes	No
4. The robin ate a worm.	Yes	No

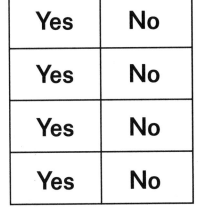

Real and Make-Believe

Week Twenty-One

③

Name

Things that are *real* happen. Things that are *make-believe* could not happen.

Is this real? Circle Yes or No.

	Yes	No
1. A tree falls on the ground.	Yes	No
2. An acorn jumps in the air.	Yes	No
3. A caterpillar turns into a butterfly.	Yes	No
4. The cup drinks some tea.	Yes	No

Real and Make-Believe

Week Twenty-One

④

Name

Things that are *real* happen. Things that are *make-believe* could not happen.

Is this make-believe? Circle Yes or No.

	Yes	No
1. The zebras lost their stripes.	Yes	No
2. The lion roared.	Yes	No
3. The tree ate a flower.	Yes	No
4. I found a key.	Yes	No

Real and Make-Believe

Week Twenty-One

(5)

Name

Things that are *real* happen. Things that are *make-believe* could not happen.

Could this happen? Circle Yes or No.

	Yes	No
1. I have a pet elephant.	Yes	No
2. Sara takes a bath.	Yes	No
3. Tony lives on the moon.	Yes	No
4. The picture talked to me.	Yes	No

Real and Make-Believe

Week Twenty-One Review

Name

Decide if the sentence is real or make-believe. Circle the correct answer.

1. The turtle ran faster than a rabbit.	Real	Make-Believe
2. The car stopped at the stop sign.	Real	Make-Believe
3. The cat climbed the tree.	Real	Make-Believe
4. A giant ate my book.	Real	Make-Believe

Possessive Nouns and Pronouns
Week Twenty-Two

1

Name

Use apostrophes in possessive nouns to show who owns something, for example, *Mom's* coat.

Find the words that match.

1. The hat that belongs to Tim   the dog's bone

2. The bone that the dog has   Tim's hat

3. The feet of the duck   the girls' shoes

4. The shoes of the girls   the duck's feet

© Weekly Reader Corp.

Possessive Nouns and Pronouns
Week Twenty-Two

2

Name

Use apostrophes in possessive nouns to show who owns something, for example, *Mom's* coat.

Draw a line under the possessive noun.

1. The tree's leaves are falling.

2. The squirrel's cheeks are full.

3. The bear's den is warm.

4. The winter's snow covers the ground.

© Weekly Reader Corp.

Possessive Nouns and Pronouns

Week Twenty-Two

3

Possessive pronouns show who or what owns something, for example, *her* coat.

Write a pronoun in the blank.

> his   its   their   her

1. Sheila said _____ lines.

2. Frank moved _____ puppet.

3. The puppet nodded _____ head.

4. The people clapped _____ hands.

Possessive Nouns and Pronouns

Week Twenty-Two

4

Possessive pronouns show who owns something, for example, *her* coat.

Circle the correct pronoun.

1. I have   **mine**   **my**   art box.

2. Bill and I will draw   **our**   **ours**   picture.

3. It is for   **Katy's**   **Katys**   birthday.

4. We will take it to   **hers**   **her**   party.

Possessive Nouns and Pronouns

Week Twenty-Two

5

Name

Use apostrophes in possessive nouns to show who owns something, for example, *Mom's* coat.

Put apostrophes where they belong.

1. Maddies race is next.

_____

2. She can hear her moms voice.

_____

3. Maddies legs move fast.

_____

4. She gets the winners prize.

_____

Possessive Nouns and Pronouns

Week Twenty-Two Review

Name

Write the sentences correctly on the lines.

1. A seals home is very cold.

_____

2. The animals favorite food is fish.

_____

3. A pups' fur is white.

_____

4. Its flippers shape helps it to swim.

_____

Alphabetical Order

Week Twenty-Three

(1)

Name

Alphabetical order is the same as ABC order. Words that begin with *a* come before words that begin with *b,* and so on.

Write the words in alphabetical order on the lines.

cat   lion   roar   Africa

_____

_____

_____

_____

Alphabetical Order

Week Twenty-Three

(2)

Name

Alphabetical order is the same as ABC order. Words that begin with *a* come before words that begin with *b,* and so on.

Are these words in alphabetical order? Circle Yes or No.

			Yes	No
1. paw	dog	train	Yes	No
2. book	pages	title	Yes	No
3. goat	horns	mountain	Yes	No
4. pet	wheel	hamster	Yes	No

Alphabetical Order

Week Twenty-Three

③

Name

Alphabetical order is the same as ABC order. Words that begin with *a* come before words that begin with *b*, and so on.

Write each list in alphabetical order on the lines.

1. rain forest _____   3. stripes _____

   frog _____   zebra _____

   tree _____   mane _____

2. trunk _____

   elephant _____

   huge _____

Alphabetical Order

Week Twenty-Three

④

Name

Alphabetical order is the same as ABC order. Words that begin with *a* come before words that begin with *b*, and so on.

Write the words in alphabetical order on the lines.

oval   circle   triangle   square

1. _____

2. _____

3. _____

4. _____

Alphabetical Order

Week Twenty-Three

⑤

Name

Alphabetical order is the same as ABC order. Words that begin with *a* come before words that begin with *b*, and so on.

Write each list in alphabetical order on the lines.

①

police   _____

vet   _____

farmer   _____

dentist   _____

②

clown   _____

nose   _____

flower   _____

parade   _____

Alphabetical Order

Week Twenty-Three Review

Name

Are these words in alphabetical order? Circle Yes or No.

				Yes	No
1. string	guitar	play		Yes	No
2. hay	cow	farm		Yes	No
3. bones	feather	wing		Yes	No
4. boat	car	train		Yes	No

Subject-Verb Agreement

Week Twenty-Four

Name _____

A singular subject names one thing. Use a singular verb. *(The girl hops.)*
A plural subject names more than one. Use a plural verb. *(The boys jump.)*

Are the sentences correct? Circle Yes or No.

	Yes	No
1. A spider spins a web.	Yes	No
2. A spider's web traps insects.	Yes	No
3. All spiders has eight legs.	Yes	No
4. Some spiders are deadly.	Yes	No

Subject-Verb Agreement

Week Twenty-Four

Name _____

A singular subject names one thing. Use a singular verb. *(The girl hops.)*
A plural subject names more than one. Use a plural verb. *(The boys jump.)*

Write the correct verb in the blank.

(is   are   shine   shines)

1. The stars _____ far away.

2. They _____ brightly.

3. The moon _____ at night too.

4. The night sky _____ beautiful.

Subject-Verb Agreement

Week Twenty-Four

③

Name

A singular subject names one thing. Use a singular verb. *(The girl hops.)*
A plural subject names more than one. Use a plural verb. *(The boys jump.)*

Are the sentences correct? Circle Yes or No.

1. Birds fly.	Yes	No
2. Girl run.	Yes	No
3. Pizzas bake.	Yes	No
4. We goes.	Yes	No

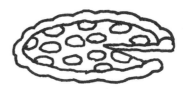

Subject-Verb Agreement

Week Twenty-Four

④

Name

A singular subject names one thing. Use a singular verb. *(The girl hops.)*
A plural subject names more than one. Use a plural verb. *(The boys jump.)*

Write each sentence correctly on the line.

1. Caterpillars turns into butterflies.

_____

2. A spider build a web.

_____

3. Insects has six legs.

_____

4. These facts is true.

_____

Subject-Verb Agreement

Week Twenty-Four

(5)

Name

A singular subject names one thing. Use a singular verb. *(The girl hops.)*
A plural subject names more than one. Use a plural verb. *(The boys jump.)*

Circle the correct verb.

1. They   **run**   **runs**   in races.

2. The races   **is**   **are**   long.

3. My brother   **swim**   **swims**   .

4. The swimmers   **is**   **are**   fast.

Subject-Verb Agreement

Week Twenty-Four Review

Name

Write each sentence correctly on the line.

1. Rain fall from clouds.

_____

2. The raindrops makes a puddle.

_____

3. The sun come out.

_____

4. It dry up the rain.

_____

Monthly Review

Name

A. Write each sentence correctly on the line.

1. Tom write a report about armadillos.

   _____

2. The armadillos shell is hard.

   _____

3. It protect the armadillo.

   _____

4. I like him report.

   _____

B. Put the words in alphabetical order. Write them on the lines.

water   _____

firefighter _____

hose   _____

ladder   _____

C. Read the sentence below. Is it real or make-believe?
   Draw a picture to show what is happening.

The pig read a book. ____ Real   ____ Make-Believe

Synonyms and Antonyms

Week Twenty-Five

1

Name

Synonyms are words that have the same meaning.

Match the words that mean the same.

1. go   little

2. happy   step

3. walk   glad

4. small   leave

Synonyms and Antonyms

Week Twenty-Five

2

Name

Antonyms are words with opposite meanings.

Write a word that means the opposite.

1. low   _____

2. wet   _____

3. awake   _____

4. light   _____

Synonyms and Antonyms

Week Twenty-Five

3

Name

Antonyms are words with opposite meanings.

**Choose a word from the box that means the opposite.
Write it on the line.**

> go   clean   far   back

1. front   _____

2. dirty   _____

3. stop   _____

4. near   _____

Synonyms and Antonyms

Week Twenty-Five

4

Name

Synonyms are words that have the same meaning.

**Choose a word from the box that means the same.
Write it on the line.**

> little   huge   watch   ball

1. big   _____

2. dance   _____

3. small   _____

4. look   _____

Synonyms and Antonyms

Week Twenty-Five

5

Name

Synonyms are words that have the same meaning. Antonyms are words with opposite meanings.

Do these words mean the same or opposite?

			Same	Opposite
1.	old	new	_____	_____
2.	big	large	_____	_____
3.	far	near	_____	_____
4.	fast	speedy	_____	_____

Synonyms and Antonyms

Week Twenty-Five Review

Name

Write the correct sentence on the line.

1. The opposite of *new* is *baby.*

_____

2. *Angry* means the same as *happy.*

_____

3. *Sack* means the same as *coat.*

_____

4. The opposite of *fast* is *quick.*

_____

Verb Forms

Week Twenty-Six

1

Name

Verbs in the present tense show that something is happening now. I *walk* to school.
Verbs in the past tense show something that already happened. I *walked* to school.

Circle the correct past tense verb.

1. I **watched** **watches** the bee.

2. It **buzz** **buzzed** around the flowers.

3. It **landed** **land** on the red one.

4. The bee **look** **looked** very busy!

Verb Forms

Week Twenty-Six

2

Name

Verbs in the present tense show that something is happening now. I *walk* to school.
Verbs in the past tense show something that already happened. I *walked* to school.

Is the sentence correct? Circle Yes or No.

1. Yesterday, we discover a bobcat.	Yes	No
2. It growled loudly.	Yes	No
3. It stayed in a cave.	Yes	No
4. My sister call for help.	Yes	No

Verb Forms

Week Twenty-Six

3

Name

Verbs in the present tense show that something is happening now. I *walk* to school.
Verbs in the past tense show something that already happened. I *walked* to school.

Finish each sentence.

1. Today they call. Last week they _____.

2. Yesterday I asked. Today I _____.

3. Today you talk. Yesterday you _____.

4. Today we help. Last month we _____.

Verb Forms

Week Twenty-Six

4

Name

Verbs in the present tense show that something is happening now. I *walk* to school.
Verbs in the past tense show something that already happened. I *walked* to school.

Write the correct verb on the line.

1. Yesterday, we _____ to the beach.
   walk   walked

2. Then we _____ pictures in the sand.
   trace   traced

3. Today, we _____ up shells.
   pick   picked

4. Now we _____ in the ocean.
   splash   splashed

Verb Forms

Week Twenty-Six

5

Name _____

Verbs in the present tense show that something is happening now. I *walk* to school.
Verbs in the past tense show something that already happened. I *walked* to school.

Is the sentence correct? Circle Yes or No.

1. We plant sunflowers in the garden last spring.

Yes	No

2. The stems reached up to the sky.

Yes	No

3. Then the seeds turned dark.

Yes	No

4. Now, we gathered the seeds.

Yes	No

Verb Forms

Week Twenty-Six Review

Name _____

Write each sentence correctly on the line.

1. Four deer trot past me last night.

_____

2. Then they jump over the fence.

_____

3. One deer wait in the garden.

_____

4. It watch the others.

_____

Spelling

Week Twenty-Seven

1

Name

Many words follow a spelling pattern.

Circle the word that is described.

1. Pull gently	tuhg	tg	tug
2. Something that burns	fyre	fire	fighr
3. Opposite of *least*	moast	mohst	most
4. Opposite of *big*	litl	little	littel

Spelling

Week Twenty-Seven

2

Name

Many words follow a spelling pattern.

Circle the word that is spelled correctly.

1. from   frum
2. wir   were
3. thenk   think
4. does   dous

Spelling

Week Twenty-Seven

3

Name

Many words follow a spelling pattern.

Write the correct verb on the line.

1. My sister got a new _____.
   dol   doll

2. Don't _____ the milk!
   spill   spil

3. Our _____ works hard!
   clas   class

4. Please _____ me.
   call   coll

Spelling

Week Twenty-Seven

4

Name

Many words follow a spelling pattern.

Look at each set of words.
Circle the word that is spelled correctly.

1. just   jist   juste

2. pand   pon   pond

3. yrd   yard   yahrd

4. there   ther   thair

Spelling

Week Twenty-Seven

5

Name

Many words follow a spelling pattern.

Circle the word that is spelled correctly.

1. Opposite of *young*   ol   olde   old

2. Angry   med   mad   madd

3. Opposite of *on*   offe   of   off

4. A big boat    ship   shipp   chip

Spelling

Week Twenty-Seven Review

Name

Write each sentence correctly on the line.

1. James has a noo backpack.

   _____

2. Pleese take this to school.

   _____

3. She wants to go whith you.

   _____

4. Do you need hep?

   _____

Compound Words

Week Twenty-Eight

1

Name

A compound word combines two words to make one. *Something* is made from the words *some* and *thing*.

Write a compound word for each pair of words.

1. table + cloth = _____

2. sun + rise = _____

3. dog + house = _____

4. cup + cake = _____

Compound Words

Week Twenty-Eight

2

Name

A compound word combines two words to make one. *Something* is made from the words *some* and *thing*.

Make compound words. Combine words from the box with words on the lines.

walk   ball   plane   room

1. lunch _____

2. snow _____

3. side _____

4. air _____

Compound Words

Week Twenty-Eight

3

Name

A compound word combines two words to make one. **Something** is made from the words *some* and *thing*.

Are these compound words? Circle Yes or No.

1. birdhouse	Yes	No
2. apple	Yes	No
3. firewood	Yes	No
4. cowboy	Yes	No

Compound Words

Week Twenty-Eight

4

Name

A compound word combines two words to make one. **Something** is made from the words *some* and *thing*.

Circle the compound word.

1. artwork   artplay

2. bluebird   bluesky

3. panlid   pancake

4. downcity   downtown

Compound Words

Week Twenty-Eight

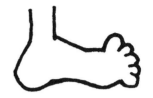

5

Name _____

A compound word combines two words to make one. *Something* is made from the words *some* and *thing*.

Make a compound word.

1. foot _____

2. sun _____

3. bed _____

4. any _____

Compound Words

Week Twenty-Eight Review

Name _____

Circle the compound words.

1. We use placemats on the table.

2. May I look at your songbook?

3. A parrot needs a large birdcage.

4. I see fingerprints on the window.

Monthly Review

Name

7

Read each clue. Write the word next to the correct number in the puzzle.

Across

1. School work done at home

3. A word that means *twist*

5. The opposite of *day*

Down

1. Another word for *cap*

2. The opposite of *young*

4. Today it rains. Yesterday it _____

Adjectives

Week Twenty-Nine

1

Name

An adjective is a word that describes something. *Smart, green,* and *fun* describe people, places, or things.

Is the word an adjective? Circle Yes or No.

1. ripe	Yes	No
2. riddle	Yes	No
3. fast	Yes	No
4. red	Yes	No

Adjectives

Week Twenty-Nine

2

Name

An adjective is a word that describes something. *Smart, green,* and *fun* describe people, places, or things.

Which word is an adjective? Circle it.

1. desk   wet

2. helps   favorite

3. shiny   frog

4. old   jump

Adjectives

Week Twenty-Nine

3

Name

An adjective is a word that describes something. *Smart*, *green*, and *fun* describe people, places, or things.

Draw a line under the adjective in each sentence.

1. A brown rabbit hopped past.

2. It went down a small hole.

3. The rabbit has a safe home.

4. It has many babies to care for.

Adjectives

Week Twenty-Nine

4

Name

An adjective is a word that describes something. *Smart*, *green*, and *fun* describe people, places, or things.

Choose an adjective from the box to complete each sentence.

| excellent   Strong   large   interesting |

1. The bald eagle is an _____ bird.

2. Eagles have _____ eyesight.

3. Eagles build _____ nests.

4. _____ laws keep the eagles safe.

Adjectives

Week Twenty-Nine

5

Name

An adjective is a word that describes something. *Smart, green,* and *fun* describe people, places, or things.

Which word is an adjective? Circle it.

1. pink   cut   draw

2. rock   flat   throw

3. tree   grow   big

4. mouse   young   sit

Adjectives

Week Twenty-Nine Review

Name

Find two adjectives in each sentence. Write them on the lines.

1. The old orange cat went outside.

   _____

2. The soft spring winds blew in the trees.

   _____

3. The tired cat fell asleep in the warm sunshine.

   _____

4. She dreamed of fat, tasty mice.

   _____

Research

Week Thirty

1

The title of the book tells what it is about. The person who wrote the book is the author.

Write the answer in the blank.

A Silkworm's Life	Rocket Girl	Fun in the Garden
by M. T. Smith	by Amy French	by Alex Potts

1. Who wrote <u>Fun in the Garden</u>? _____

2. Which did Amy French write? _____

3. Which might tell about flowers? _____

4. Who wrote <u>A Silkworm's Life</u>? _____

Research

Week Thirty

2

Words in a dictionary are in alphabetical order.

Look at each word. Circle *front, middle,* or *back* to tell where it is in a dictionary.

1. cowboy: front   middle   back

2. leather: front   middle   back

3. horse: front   middle   back

4. western: front   middle   back

Research

Week Thirty

3

The Table of Contents tells what is in a book.

Look at the Table of Contents below. Then answer the questions.

All About Frogs		
Chapter 1	Where Frogs Live	Page 2
Chapter 2	From Tadpoles to Frogs	Page 6
Chapter 3	Types of Frogs	Page 12

1. What chapter tells you where frogs live? _____
2. On what page does Chapter 2 start? _____
3. What chapter might tell about tree frogs? _____
4. Write the title of the book. _____

Research

Week Thirty

4

Words in a dictionary are in alphabetical order.

Look at each word. Tell whether you would look for it in the front, middle, or back of the dictionary.

1. Earth: front   middle   back

2. Sun: front   middle   back

3. Moon: front   middle   back

4. Venus: front   middle   back

Research

Week Thirty

5

Name

The title of the book tells what it is about. The person who wrote the book is the author.

Write the answer in the blank.

Soccer!	Our World	Ocean Animals
by	by	by
Javier Ortiz	Frances Lee	Taylor Dixon

1. Who wrote <u>Ocean Animals</u>? _____

2. What is the title of Frances Lee's book?

_____

3. Which book is about sports? _____

4. Who wrote <u>Soccer!</u>? _____

Research

Week Thirty Review

Name

Words in a dictionary are in alphabetical order.

Look at each word. Tell whether you would look for it in the front, middle, or back of the dictionary.

1. monkey: **front**   **middle**   **back**

2. tiger: **front**   **middle**   **back**

3. elephant: **front**   **middle**   **back**

4. camel: **front**   **middle**   **back**

Reading Charts, Graphs, and Diagrams

Week Thirty-One

1

Name _____

You can get information from charts, graphs, and diagrams.

Read each question. Use the weather chart to find the answer.

Monday	Tuesday	Wednesday	Thursday	Friday
rain	cloudy	snow	partly cloudy	sunny

1. What was the weather on Tuesday? _____

2. When did it snow? _____

3. Which day was sunny? _____

4. What was the weather on Monday? _____

Reading Charts, Graphs, and Diagrams

Week Thirty-One

2

Name _____

Charts, graphs, and diagrams provide information.

Our Favorite Apples

Red	🧍🧍🧍🧍🧍🧍🧍🧍🧍
Yellow	🧍🧍🧍🧍🧍
Green	🧍🧍

🧍 = 1 child

Look at the graph. Circle the correct answer.

	red	green	yellow
1. Which apple did most children pick?			
2. How many children picked green apples?	5	2	8
3. How many children picked red apples?	2	5	9
4. Did more choose yellow or green apples?		yellow	green

Reading Charts, Graphs, and Diagrams

Week Thirty-One

3

Name

Charts, graphs, and diagrams provide information.

The graph shows the kinds of bugs Amy found. Use the graph to answer the questions.

Ants	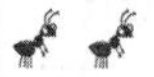 🐜 🐜
Beetles	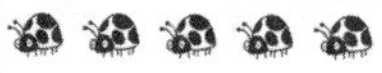 🐞 🐞 🐞 🐞 🐞
Crickets	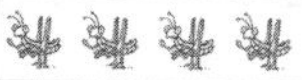 🦗 🦗 🦗 🦗

1. How many crickets did Amy find? _____

2. Did Amy find more ants or beetles? _____

3. How many bugs did Amy find altogether? _____

4. Amy found 2 of which kind of bug? _____

Reading Charts, Graphs, and Diagrams

Week Thirty-One

4

Name

Charts, graphs, and diagrams provide information.

Where Animals Live

Desert	Rain Forest	Ocean
roadrunner	monkey	octopus
coyote	parrot	starfish
pack rat	anteater	eel

Use the chart to find the answer. Circle the answer.

1. Where do parrots live?   rain forest   desert

2. Which animal lives in the ocean?   coyote   eel

3. Where would you find a pack rat?   rain forest   desert

4. Which animal lives in the rain forest?   anteater   starfish

Reading Charts, Graphs, and Diagrams

Week Thirty-One

5

Name

Charts, graphs, and diagrams provide information.

Riding the Bus

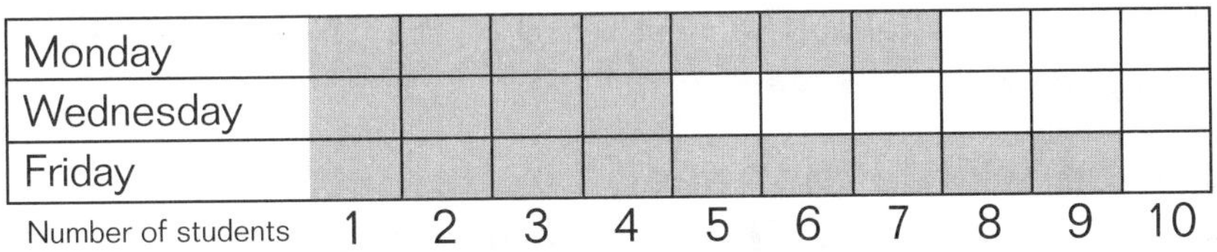

	1	2	3	4	5	6	7	8	9	10
Monday										
Wednesday										
Friday										

Number of students 1 2 3 4 5 6 7 8 9 10

The graph shows how many students rode the bus each day. Use it to answer the questions. Circle your answer.

1. When did the most students ride the bus?   Monday   Friday

2. When did 4 students ride the bus?   Wednesday   Friday

3. How many rode on Monday?   6   7

4. Did more students ride on Monday or Wednesday?   Monday   Wednesday

---

Reading Charts, Graphs, and Diagrams

Week Thirty-One Review

Name

Taste Test

Grapes	👧👧👧👧👧👧👧👧
Kiwi	👧👧👧👧👧👧👧👧👧
Oranges	👧👧👧👧

👧 = 1 child

The graph shows how many children like each fruit. Use the graph to answer the questions.

1. How many children like oranges? _____

2. What fruit did the children like best? _____

3. Did more choose grapes than oranges? _____

4. How many children like kiwi? _____

Friendly Letters

Week Thirty-Two

1

Name

Capitalize the words in the greeting of a friendly letter. For example:
Dear Aunt Lucy. Capitalize the first word of the closing and the signature.
For example: *Yours truly, Sam.*

Circle the words that need capital letters in the greeting and closing of this letter.

> 453 Oak Street
> Trenton, NJ 55555
> February 12, 2006
>
> dear uncle jim,
>   I am glad you came to see us! Your stories really made me laugh. Please come back soon.
>
>   love,
>   annie

Friendly Letters

Week Thirty-Two

2

Name

Put a comma after the greeting of a friendly letter. For example:
Dear Aunt Lucy, Put a comma after the closing. For example: *Yours truly,*

Add commas to the greeting and closing.
Do not forget the commas in the address and date.

> 123 Main St.
> Wichita KS 55555
> June 18 2006
>
> Dear Mrs. Jones
>   I just read the book you wrote. It was great! I loved how Jesse solved his problems.
>
>   Sincerely
>   Jack Morris

Friendly Letters

Week Thirty-Two

3

Name

Capitalize the words in the greeting of a friendly letter. For example:
Dear Aunt Lucy. Capitalize the first word of the closing and the signature.
For example: *Yours truly, Sam.*

Circle the words that need capital letters in the greeting and closing.

14807 Lake Blvd.
Denver, CO 55555
Nov. 1, 2006

dear grandma,

   Are you coming to our house for Thanksgiving this year? We're going to make your favorite pies! Please come.

love always,
cassie

Friendly Letters

Week Thirty-Two

4

Name

Put a comma after the greeting of a friendly letter. For example:
Dear Aunt Lucy, Put a comma after the closing as well. For example: *Yours truly,*

Add commas to the greeting and closing of this letter.
Do not forget the commas in the address and date.

805 Duke Ave.
Austin TX 55555
May 4 2006

Dear Luke

   We are going camping this year for my birthday. I would like you to come with us. Do you think you can?

Your friend
Jake

Friendly Letters

Week Thirty-Two

5

Name _____

Capitalize the words in the greeting of a friendly letter. For example:
Dear Aunt Lucy. Capitalize the first word of the closing and the signature.
For example: *Yours truly, Sam.*

**Finish the friendly letter. Use commas
and capitals in the greeting and closing.**

605 Seaspray
Beachside, CA 55555
July 25, 2006

_____

   We are having lots of fun! The beach is great.
We even saw dolphins.

         _____

         _____

Friendly Letters

Week Thirty-Two Review

Name _____

**Find the mistakes. Circle the words that should be capitalized.
Add commas where needed.**

1400 Chalk Rd.
Spring, FL 55555
October 10, 2006

Dear aunt maggie
   Thanks for remembering my birthday. You know how
much I like to read! The book is terrific!

       love
       kevin

Monthly Review

Name

A. Circle the adjectives in each sentence.

1. The giant owl flew through the dark sky.
2. It caught the scared little mouse.

B. Circle the words that need capitals. Add commas where needed. Circle the title of a book.

1400 Chalk Rd.
48 river road
Memphis, TN 55555
june 18 2006

dear Uncle jay
   I can't wait to go camping next month! I've already read <u>Stars</u> by Seymour Simon.

       love
       andrea

C. Use the graph to answer the questions.

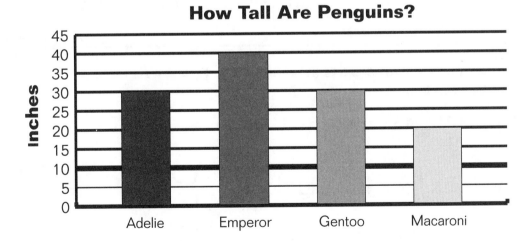

How Tall Are Penguins?

1. Which penguin is as tall as Adelie? _____
2. Which penguin is the tallest? _____
3. Which penguin is the shortest? _____

Grammar Review

Week Thirty-Three

Name _____

A noun is a person, place, or thing. *Girl, school,* and *bike* are all nouns.

Draw a line under the noun in each sentence.

1. I found a rock.

2. It was in the creek.

3. The stone is flat.

4. The water made it smooth.

Grammar Review

Week Thirty-Three

Name _____

A verb shows action or being. *Climb* is an action verb. *Is, are, was, were,* and *am* are verbs of being.

Draw a line under the verb in each sentence.

1. Gray wolves look like big dogs.

2. They live in packs.

3. They hunt deer.

4. Some wolves have four pups.

Grammar Review

Week Thirty-Three

3

Name _____

A singular subject names one thing. Use a singular verb. *(The girl hops.)*
A plural subject names more than one. Use a plural verb. *(The boys jump.)*

Circle the correct word.

1. Snowflakes _____ made of ice.
   is   are

2. They _____ in clouds.
   grow   grows

3. Each snowflake _____ different.
   is   are

4. This snowflake _____ six points.
   has   have

Grammar Review

Week Thirty-Three

4

Name _____

Pronouns replace nouns in a sentence.

Choose the correct word for each sentence.

1. Kay and _____ wrote a story.
   I   me

2. _____ wanted it to be about cats.
   Her   She

3. _____ I wanted it to be about dogs.
   Me   I

4. _____ wrote about cats and dogs.
   We   Us

Grammar Review

Week Thirty-Three

5

Name

Nouns that stand for one thing are singular. *Dog* is a singular noun. Nouns that stand for more than one thing are plural. *Dogs* is a plural noun.

Write each word in the box in the correct column below.

girls   child   men   foot   tooth   mice

One

More than One

_____   _____

_____   _____

_____   _____

Grammar Review

Week Thirty-Three Review

Name

Write each sentence correctly on the line.

1. Sofia and me have loose teeth.

_____

2. Eric lost a teeth last year.

_____

3. A new tooth growed.

_____

4. I can't wait for me new tooth!

Capitalization Review

Week Thirty-Four   1

Name

Titles of books and magazines are capitalized. Always capitalize the first, last, and any important words.

Add capital letters. Write each sentence correctly on the line.

1. eric carle writes books.

_____

2. He wrote <u>the very hungry caterpillar</u>.

_____

3. I like to read <u>the grouchy ladybug</u>.

_____

Capitalization Review

Week Thirty-Four   2

Name

Names of days, months, and holidays are always capitalized. For example: *Friday, June,* and *New Year's Day* are capitalized.

Draw a line under the words that need capital letters.

1. mother's day is in May.

2. earth day is April 22.

3. Father's Day is always on sunday.

4. We love valentine's day!

Capitalization Review

Week Thirty-Four

3

Name

Names of places are always capitalized.

Add capital letters. Write the sentences correctly on the lines.

1. I live in the city of mobile.

   _____

2. My state is alabama.

   _____

3. The united states is my country.

   _____

4. I live in america.

   _____

Capitalization Review

Week Thirty-Four

4

Name

People's names and titles are always capitalized. *Mr., Ms.,* and *Dr.* are titles. Names of places are always capitalized.

Draw a line under the words that need capital letters.

1. willie mays loved baseball.

2. He grew up in birmingham, alabama.

3. He played for the new york Giants.

4. mays hit many home runs.

Capitalization Review

Week Thirty-Four

5

Name

Names of days, months, and holidays are always capitalized. For example: *Friday, June,* and *New Year's Day* are capitalized.

Draw a line under the words that need capital letters.

1. I like spending saturday in the park.

2. We play softball there in april.

3. We watch butterflies in june.

4. Sometimes we go on sunday instead.

Capitalization Review

Week Thirty-Four Review

Name

Write each sentence correctly on the line.

1. alligators live near water.

_____

2. There are many alligators in florida.

_____

3. They build their nests in june.

_____

4. the nests hold about 30 eggs.

_____

Punctuation Review

Week Thirty-Five

1

Name

Use a period (.) at the end of a statement. Use a question mark (?) at the end of a question.

Add a period (.) or question mark (?) to each sentence.

1. Sand cats live in the desert _____

2. They don't have to drink water _____

3. They get water from their food _____

4. Aren't sand cats interesting _____

Punctuation Review

Week Thirty-Five

2

Name

Abbreviations and people's titles end with a period (.). For example: *Jan.* is the abbreviation for *January*. *Mr., Mrs., Ms.,* and *Dr.* are examples of titles.

Replace the underlined words with the correct abbreviation in the box.

> Mr.   Dr.   Mrs.   Fri.   Wed.   Feb.

1. I saw <u>Doctor</u> Frost.

2. <u>Mister</u> Lee is my teacher.

_____

3. <u>February</u> 28 is my birthday.

_____

4. <u>Wednesday</u> is the middle of the week.

_____

Punctuation Review

Week Thirty-Five

3

Name

Commas are used to separate things in a list.

Add commas to each sentence. Write it correctly on the line.

1. We buy fruit vegetables and bread.

   _____

2. I like science art and music.

   _____

3. Dogs cats hamsters and fish make good pets.

   _____

4. Our garden is full of flowers, bushes, and weeds!

   _____

Punctuation Review

Week Thirty-Five

4

Name

Commas are used in dates and addresses. Commas separate the date from the year: *October 14, 2000.* **Commas separate the city and state:** *Portland, Oregon.*

Add commas below.

1. December 31 2000

   _____

2. Ogden Utah

   _____

3. April 1 1959

   _____

4. Chicago Illinois

Punctuation Review

Week Thirty-Five

5

Name

Use an apostrophe (') in contractions and to show who owns something.

Add an apostrophe ('). Write the sentences correctly on the lines.

1. A sea otters fur keeps it warm.

_____

2. Sea otters arent quiet animals.

_____

3. Theyre very playful.

_____

4. Many otters live in Californias oceans.

_____

Punctuation Review

Week Thirty-Five Review

Name

Find seven mistakes. Add commas, periods, or question marks.

125 Madrid Dr
Tucson AZ 55555
January 1 2006

Dear Julia

   The desert is fun in the winter You should see the cactus here! Did you know that some are taller than me

                              Your friend
                              Anaya

Spelling Review

Week Thirty-Six 1

Name _____

Many words follow a spelling pattern.

Choose the word that is spelled correctly.

1. Let's play _____ school.
   after   aftur

2. Don't forget to say _____ you!
   thanke   thank

3. Please show me _____ to do that.
   how   howe

4. Where are we _____?
   going   goin

Spelling Review

Week Thirty-Six 2

Name _____

Homophones are words that sound alike but have different spellings and meanings.

Circle the correct word.

1. This is a color.	blew	blue
2. This is an insect.	be	bee
3. You can ride this animal.	horse	hoarse
4. This is a number.	won	one

Spelling Review

Week Thirty-Six

3

Name

Many words follow a spelling pattern.

Correct each sentence.

1. We sang a toon.

_____

2. Can you hope on one foot?

_____

3. Klap your hands!

_____

4. The hin laid an egg.

_____

Spelling Review

Week Thirty-Six

4

Name

Many words follow a spelling pattern.

Choose the word that is spelled correctly.

1. I am in _____ grade.

              furst   first

2. I found a bug in the _____.

               dert   dirt

3. That _____ is bright.

         star   stare

4. _____ have lots of teeth.

    Sharks   Shrks

Spelling Review

Week Thirty-Six

5

Name

Many words follow a spelling pattern.

Circle the word that is spelled correctly.

1. The color of the sun   yello   yellow

2. The number after two   three   thee

3. A place where animals live   zew   zoo

4. Opposite of *hot*   cold   kold

Spelling Review

Week Thirty-Six Review

Name

Write the sentences correctly on the lines.

1. I gav him the ball.

   _____

2. I saw him smil.

   _____

3. Then he sed good-bye.

   _____

4. I will mis him.

   _____

Monthly Review

Name

A. Find all of the mistakes. Then write each sentence correctly.

1. school often starts in september

_____

2. we eat turkey at thanksgiving?

_____

3. there are meny winter holidays

_____

4. do you like to ski in the spring.

_____

B. Follow the directions for each sentence.

Put an X by the sentence that has a NOUN underlined.

1. ____ Some dogs are trained to help <u>people</u>. Ⓝ

____ Some dogs are <u>trained</u> to help people. Ⓡ

Put an X by the sentence that has a VERB underlined.

2. ____ Seeing-eye <u>dogs</u> help people who can't see. Ⓟ

____ Seeing-eye dogs <u>help</u> people who can't see. Ⓣ

Put an X by the sentence that has an ADJECTIVE underlined.

3. ____ These wonderful dogs
<u>make</u> life easier for many people. Ⓞ

____ These <u>wonderful</u> dogs
make life easier for many people. Ⓐ

Each answer has a letter circled.
Write that letter in the correct circle below.

Why was the bug mixed up?
Because his uncle was an   ◯ ◯ ◯ !
                                 3 1 2

Daily Language Practice
Answers — Grade 1

Week 1

Day One
1. Many 2. We 3. Do 4. I

Day Two
1. When will I have a turn?
2. (You did all your work.)
3. We share with others.
4. (We like to follow the rules!)

Day Three
1. **Liz** and **I** wrote a report about penguins. 2. **Penguins** live in cold places. 3. **Some** penguins build nests out of rocks. 4. **Other** penguins hold their eggs on their feet.

Day Four
1. Some storms bring strong winds.
2. People must get ready for storms. 3. Clean water is important. 4. Food is important too.

Day Five
1. (I like apples.)
2. May I plant the seeds?
3. Mom and I picked apples.
4. (May I taste the green apple?)

Review
1. **It** rained yesterday.
2. **The** wind blew last week.
3. **Today** was cloudy.
4. **Rain** may come again tomorrow.

Week 2

Day One
1. Where do you live? 2. We live in the United States. 3. Do you know where the president lives? 4. He lives in the White House.

Day Two
1. Have you seen the American flag?
2. It is red, white, and blue. 3. (How many stars are on the flag?) 4. (The stripes are red and white.)

Day Three
1. What should you do if there is a fire**?**
2. Get out as fast as you can**.**
3. Crawl on the floor if you see smoke**.**
4. Do you have a smoke alarm**?**

Day Four
1. **?** 2. **.** 3. **.** 4. **?**

Day Five
1. **.** 2. **.** 3. **?** 4. **?**

Review
1. There is a big web outside.
2. Was the spider yellow?
3. I think it was a banana spider.
4. Do they build big webs?

Week 3

Day One

Person	Place	Thing
Mr. Hill	school	flag
students		desk

Day Two
1. house 2. Boston 3. uncle
4. John

Day Three
Answers will vary.

Day Four
1. The **(children)** are **(friends)**.
2. **(John)** reads a **(book)**.
3. **(Seth)** laughs at a funny **(story)**.
4. Soon the **(boys)** will go **(home)**.

Day Five
1. No 2. Yes 3. Yes 4. No

Review
1. Paul likes to play **(soccer)**.
2. **(Ms. Akin)** teaches us how to play.
3. **(Carlos)** kicks the **(ball)**.
4. **(Iris)** runs down the **(field)**.

Week 4

Day One
1. Lee
2. Dr. Howell
3. Clear Lake
4. Texas

Day Two
1. <u>Dr. Martin Luther King Jr.</u> was a great man. 2. He was born in <u>Atlanta.</u> 3. He marched in <u>Montgomery.</u> 4. Many people heard him speak at the <u>Lincoln Memorial.</u>

Day Three
1. America 2. food
3. Native Americans 4. corn

Day Four
1. Kim and **Luke** play together.
2. **Bob** shares his favorite game.
3. Kate helps **William.**
4. Joan tells **Maria** a story.

Day Five
Answers will vary.

Review
1. My mom walks with me to **Oak Street.**
2. I am going to see **Dr.** Lopez.
3. **Mr. James** calls my name.
4. Dr. **Lopez** looks in my ears.

Month 1 Review

A. 1. Do you like caterpillars?
2. **Caterpillars** eat plants.
3. We have caterpillars in **Mrs. Krauss's** room.
4. My friends and **I** love caterpillars!

B.

S	B	I	R	D
H	O	M	E	O
F	Y	A	H	G
O	D	V	U	L
D	E	S	K	I

Week 5

Day One
1. Yes 2. No 3. No 4. Yes

Day Two
1. Yes 2. No 3. Yes 4. No

Day Three
1. April 17, 1995
2. Jackson, Mississippi
3. May 22, 1933
4. Los Angeles, California

Day Four
1. No 2. Yes 3. Yes 4. No

Day Five
1. Fairbanks, Alaska 2. February 12, 1984 3. June 27, 2006
4. Akron, Ohio

Review
1. We waved the flag on July 4, 2006. 2. We had a picnic in Elk Falls, Kansas. 3. Thanksgiving is November 23, 2006. 4. We will go to Nashville, Tennessee.

Week 6

Day One
1. I am 2. you will 3. did not
4. here is

Day Two
1. hasn't 2. we'll
3. I've 4. isn't

Day Three
1. **(Let's)** go to the zoo.
2. **(I'd)** like to see the koalas.
3. Koalas **(aren't)** bears.
4. They **(don't)** move around much.

Day Four
1. I <u>won't</u> eat candy.
2. <u>I'd</u> rather be healthy!
3. <u>I'll</u> eat good foods.
4. <u>Don't</u> you want to join me?

Day Five
1. <u>Here's</u> my wish.
2. <u>I'd</u> like to fly an airplane.
3. <u>I'll</u> fly in the clouds.
4. <u>They're</u> so fast!

Review
1. **You'd** like this book.
2. **It's** about the rain forest.
3. **Here's** a picture of blue frogs.
4. You **wouldn't** want to touch one!

Week 7
Day One

One	More than One
eye	webs
moth	homes
leg	bugs

Day Two
1. Spiders 2. legs 3. bugs
4. spider

Day Three
1. insect 2. butterfly 3. flower
4. grasshopper

Day Four
1. cows 2. snakes 3. horses
4. dolphins

Day Five
1. I read a book about **(kangaroos)**.
2. They have strong **(legs)**.
3. The **(babies)** are called **(joeys)**.
4. They live in **(pouches)**.

Review
1. Rain **forests** are in danger.
2. **People** cut down many tree.
3. They build **roads** and farms.
4. That hurts the plants and **animals**.

Week 8
Day One
1. St.
2. Mr.
3. Rd.
4. Dr.

Day Two
1. Ms. Sarah Fallen
   146 Main St.
2. Dr. Kim Lee
   932 Lake Ave.

Day Three
1. No 2. Yes 3. No 4. No

Day Four
To: Mrs. Jane Barnes
When: Sat., Feb. 14
Where: 27 Duke St.
What: Valentine's Day Party!

Day Five
1. Mon.
2. Aug.
3. Nov.
4. Wed.

Review
1. Dr. Jen Tyler
2. 556 Lake Rd.
3. Mr. Pat Lewis
4. Oct. 31

Month 2 Review
A. 1. My family went to Sarasota, Florida. 2. We stayed with Dr. Reyes and her family. 3. We saw sand, shells, and dolphins. 4. I've got some beautiful shells.

B.

One	More than One
dog	dresses
snake	songs
ant	cars

Week 9
Day One
1. Our class has art on **Monday.**
2. We go to music on **Tuesday.**
3. We have a field trip next **Thursday.**
4. I will be the leader on **Friday.**

Day Two
1. I plant seeds in **(april)**.
2. Flowers bloom in **(may)**.
3. Tomatoes grow in **(june)**.
4. We pick pumpkins in **(october)**.

Day Three
1. It is cold in **(january)**.
2. It snowed last **(monday)**.
3. We made a snowman on **(tuesday)**.
4. I wonder if **(february)** will be cold.

Day Four
1. day 2. January 3. Chinese New Year 4. Sunday

Day Five
1. February 2 is <u>groundhog day.</u>
2. Many people like <u>valentine's day.</u>
3. Do you play tricks on <u>april fool's day?</u> 4. We had a piñata on <u>cinco de mayo.</u>

Review
1. We celebrate many American **holidays.** 2. **Presidents' Day** is in February. 3. Memorial Day is the last **Monday** in May. 4. Many people eat turkey on **Thanksgiving.**

Week 10
Day One
1. Milk, yogurt, and cheese build strong bones. 2. Bread, pasta, rice, and cereal are good to eat. 3. Candy, cookies, and cake are not good for you.

Day Two
1. Tom plays baseball, soccer, and basketball. 2. Samantha likes math, art, and reading.

Day Three
1. Yes 2. No 3. Yes 4. Yes

Day Four
1. Kim picked up rocks, feathers, and shells. 2. She put them in boxes, cups, and buckets. 3. Kim found yellow, white, and pink rocks. 4. The feathers were brown, gray, black, and blue.

Day Five
1. No 2. Yes 3. Yes 4. No

Review
1. We eat the roots of carrots, onions, and beets.
2. We eat lettuce, spinach, and cabbage leaves.
3. Corn, beans, and nuts are seeds.
4. We eat the roots, leaves, and seeds of plants.

Week 11
Day One
1. Dogs are good pets.
2. They are friendly.
3. Dogs like to play.
4. They like to be petted.

Day Two
1. Yes 2. No 3. Yes 4. No

Day Three
1. play 2. while 3. yourself
4. bike

Day Four
1. No 2. No 3. No 4. Yes

Day Five
1. life 2. fish 3. So 4. are

Review
1. It snowed today. 2. Where is your coat? 3. Where are your mittens?
4. Let's make a snowman!

Week 12
Day One
1. map 2. Can 3. bus 4. not
Day Two
1. lake 2. nose 3. bite 4. cute
Day Three
1. Birds come to the feeder **(evry)** day. 2. They **(et)** the seeds.
3. A cat watches **(thim)**. 4. The birds **(fli)** away.

Day Four
1. over 2. pet 3. open 4. five
Day Five
1. Brown 2. live 3. dig 4. Some
Review
1. Summer can be **hot.** 2. You need to **take** care of your dog.
3. **Give** him lots of clean water.
4. Go for a walk **when** it is cool.

Month 3 Review
A. 1. We go to the circus on July 8, 2006. 2. We have fun at the circus. 3. The clown **makes** us laugh. 4. **Some** clowns drive cars.
B. January, March, May, July, August, October

Week 13
Day One
1. No 2. Yes 3. Yes 4. No
Day Two
1. The Big Book of Snakes
2. Under the Sea
3. A Letter from Home
4. A Hat for a Hen
Day Three
1. I love to read Sheep in a Jeep.
2. Our class likes to read Your Big Backyard. 3. I like The Cat in the Hat.
Day Four
1. Yes 2. No 3. No 4. No
Day Five
1. The Life of a Frog
2. Looking for Rainbows
3. The Sky High House
4. The Story of Silk
Review
1. My brother likes to read Hop on Pop.
2. Have you read Mike and the Bike?
3. Duck on a Bike will make you laugh!
4. I just read Farmer in the Dell.

Week 14
Day One
1. kick 2. swim 3. blow 4. run
Day Two
1. Yes 2. No 3. Yes 4. Yes
Day Three
1. Penguins **(hunt)** for food in the ocean.
2. Penguins **(dive)** into the cold water.
3. Their feathers **(keep)** them warm.
4. Some penguins **(build)** nests of rocks.

Day Four
Answers will vary.
Day Five
1. No 2. Yes 3. Yes 4. No
Review
1. Many people **(eat)** oranges.
2. Oranges **(grow)** in warm places.
3. Oranges **(turn)** orange when it is cold.
4. Oranges **(stay)** green in hot weather.

Week 15
Day One
1. No 2. Yes 3. No 4. Yes
Day Two
Answers will vary.
Day Three
1. Yes 2. No 3. No 4. Yes
Day Four
Answers will vary
Day Five
1. No 2. Yes 3. No 4. Yes
Review
1. plays baseball.
2. helps him catch the ball.
3. is hard to hit the ball.
4. practice too.

Week 16
Day One
1. I 2. He 3. She 4. It
Day Two
1. we 2. It 3. I 4. We
Day Three
1. it 2. them 3. me 4. us
Day Four
1. Will **(you)** sing **(me)** a song?
2. **(They)** like **(me).**
3. **(She)** and **(I)** run races.
4. Can **(he)** go with **(us)?**
Day Five
1. He read a book
   John read it.
2. She followed Bill home.
   The cat followed him home.
Review
1. Julia and **I** went to the movies.
2. **They** are friends. 3. **She** likes to write. 4. **Cheryl and I** are in the story. (OR **We** are in the story.)

Month 4 Review
1. Kangaroos jump with strong legs. **(S)**
2. Jimmy and I went to the zoo. **(P)**
3. I read Where the Wild Things Are. **(I)**
4. The brown bear was very tall. **(N)**
Why are spiders like tops? Because they **S P I N** .

Week 17
Day One
1. The eagle **(flies).**
2. The dolphin **(dives)** into the water.
3. Ducks **(waddle)** away.
4. The monkey **(swings)** in the tree.
Day Two
1. My friends **(are)** taller than me.
2. The puppy **(was)** cute.
3. I **(am)** happy.
4. The kittens **(were)** sleepy.
Day Three
1. Our class **(wrote)** a play.
2. I **(am)** the queen.
3. Alex **(is)** the king.
4. He **(sings)** a song.
Day Four
1. Yes 2. Yes 3. No 4. Yes
Day Five
1. A beaver builds a home.
2. It uses mud and sticks.
3. The home is near the water.
4. Beavers are good swimmers.
Review
1. Ellen and Sam **(help)** at home.
2. They **(clean)** their rooms.
3. They **(hang)** their clothes up.
4. The children **(are)** helpful.

Week 18
Day One
1. **(feed)**	frog	**(seed)**
2. log	**(goat)**	**(boat)**
3. **(jar)**	**(star)**	lug
4. lick	**(mop)**	**(hop)**
Day Two
1. stick 2. well 3. look 4. tall
Day Three
Answers will vary.
Day Four
1. No 2. Yes 3. No 4. Yes
Day Five
1. **(chop)**	map	**(hop)**
2. **(slip)**	drop	**(drip)**
3. fall	**(fill)**	**(pill)**
4. **(wall)**	**(ball)**	well
Review
1. sky 2. stink 3. house 4. How

Week 19
Day One
Things in the Sky
star sun moon
Things on the Ground
ant tree grass
Day Two
1. birds 2. bee 3. kite 4. plane
Day Three
1. No 2. No 3. Yes 4. Yes

Day Four
1. No 2. Yes 3. No 4. Yes
Day Five
(Answers may vary.)
Things that live in water   Plants
Review

Things We Eat	Living Things
nuts	~~ears~~
apples	people
~~grass~~	~~rocks~~
cheese	cats
~~dirt~~	~~sunflowers~~

Week 20
Day One
1. glad 2. clap 3. flat 4. snap
Day Two
1. are 2. your 3. bark 4. bird
Day Three
1. quack 2. duck 3. rock 4. walk
Day Four
1. I went to the **park** to play.
2. It was my **turn** on the swing.
3. I fell in the **dirt.** 4. I **hurt** my arm.
Day Five
1. spin 2. slip 3. ant 4. frog
Review
1. **Sharks** swim in the ocean.
2. Watch the bird **flap** its wings!
3. The **chick** peeped loudly.
4. The farmer's **crop** grew fast.

Month 5 Review
A. 1. We see many **stars** at night.
2. The sun **is** a star too.
3. All stars **are** made of gases.
4. They are **very** hot.
B. Answers will vary.
C.

L	L	A	M	A	O
O	B	M	O	N	T
H	E	N	O	T	T
A	E	K	S	C	E
R	S	**B**	**E**	**A**	**R**

Week 21
Day One
1. No 2. No 3. Yes 4. Yes
Day Two
1. No 2. Yes 3. Yes 4. No
Day Three
1. Yes 2. No 3. Yes 4. No
Day Four
1. Yes 2. No 3. Yes 4. No
Day Five
1. No 2. Yes 3. No 4. No
Review
1. Make-believe 2. Real
3. Real 4. Make-believe

Week 22
Day One
1. Tim's hat
2. The dog's bone
3. The duck's feet
4. The girls' shoes
Day Two
1. The <u>tree's</u> leaves are falling.
2. The <u>squirrel's</u> cheeks are full.
3. The <u>bear's</u> den is warm.
4. The <u>winter's</u> snow covers the ground.
Day Three
1. Sheila said <u>her</u> lines.
2. Frank moved <u>his</u> puppet.
3. The puppet nodded <u>its</u> head.
4. The people clapped <u>their</u> hands.
Day Four
1. my 2. our 3. Katy's 4. her
Day Five
1. **Maddie's** race is next.
2. She can hear her **mom's** voice.
4. **Maddie's** legs move fast.
5. She gets the **winner's** prize.
Review
1. A **seal's** home is very cold.
2. The **animal's** (OR **animals'**) favorite food is fish.
3. A pup's fur is white.
4. Its **flipper's** shape helps it to swim.

Week 23
Day One
Africa cat lion roar
Day Two
1. No 2. Yes 3. Yes 4. No
Day Three
1. frog, rain forest, tree
2. elephant, huge, trunk
3. mane, stripes, zebra
Day Four
circle oval square triangle
Day Five
1. dentist, farmer, police, vet
2. clown, flower, nose, parade
Review
1. No 2. No 3. Yes 4. Yes

Week 24
Day One
1. Yes 2. Yes 3. No 4. Yes
Day Two
1. are 2. shine 3. shines 4. is
Day Three
1. Yes 2. No 3. Yes 4. No
Day Four
1. Caterpillars **turn** into butterflies.
2. A spider **builds** a web.
3. Insects **have** six legs.

4. These facts **are** true.
Day Five
1. run 2. are 3. swims 4. are
Review
1. Rain **falls** from clouds.
2. The raindrops **make** a puddle.
3. The sun **comes** out.
4. It **dries** up the rain.

Month 6 Review
A. 1. Tom **writes** a report about armadillos. 2. The **armadillo's** shell is hard. 3. It **protects** the armadillo.
4. I like **his** report.
B. firefighter hose ladder water
C. Pictures will vary.
1. Make-Believe

Week 25
Day One
1. leave 2. glad 3. step 4. little
Day Two
1. high 2. dry 3. asleep 4. dark
Day Three
1. back 2. clean 3. go 4. far
Day Four
1. huge 2. ball 3. little 4. watch
Day Five
1. Opposite 2. Same
3. Opposite 4. Same
Review
Answers may vary.
1. The opposite of *new* is **old**.
2. *Angry* means the same as **mad**.
3. *Sack* means the same as **bag**.
4. The opposite of *fast* is **slow**.

Week 26
Day One
1. watched 2. buzzed
3. landed 4. looked
Day Two
1. No 2. Yes 3. Yes 4. No
Day Three
1. called 2. ask 3. talked 4. helped
Day Four
1. walked 2. traced 3. pick 4. splash
Day Five
1. No 2. Yes 3. Yes 4. No
Review
1. Four deer **trotted** past me last night. 2. Then they **jumped** over the fence. 3. One deer **waited** in the garden. 4. It **watched** the others.

Week 27
Day One
1. tug 2. fire 3. most 4. little
Day Two
1. from 2. were 3. think 4. does

Day Three
1. doll 2. spill 3. class 4. call
Day Four
1. just 2. pond 3. yard 4. there
Day Five
1. old 2. mad 3. off 4. ship
Review
1. James has a **new** backpack.
2. **Please** take this to school.
3. She wants to go **with** you.
4. Do you need **help?**

Week 28
Day One
1. tablecloth 2. sunrise
3. doghouse 4. cupcake
Day Two
1. lunchroom 2. snowball
3. sidewalk 4. airplane
Day Three
1. Yes 2. No 3. Yes 4. Yes
Day Four
1. artwork 2. bluebird
3. pancake 4. downtown
Day Five
Answers will vary.
Review
1. We use **(placemats)** on the table.
2. May I look at your **(songbook)?**
3. A parrot needs a large **(birdcage).**
4. I see **(fingerprints)** on the window.

Month 7 Review
```
H O M E W O R K
A         L
T U R N   D
  A
  I
  N   I G H T
  E
  D
```

Week 29
Day One
1. Yes 2. No 3. Yes 4. Yes
Day Two
1. wet 2. favorite 3. shiny 4. old
Day Three
1. A <u>brown</u> rabbit hopped past.
2. It went down a <u>small</u> hole.
3. The rabbit has a <u>safe</u> home.
4. It has <u>many</u> babies to care for.
Day Four
1. interesting 2. excellent
3. large 4. strong
Day Five
1. pink 2. flat 3. big 4. young
Review
1. old, orange 2. soft, spring
3. tired, warm 4. fat, tasty

Week 30
Day One
1. Alex Potts 2. <u>Rocket Girl</u>
3. <u>Fun in the Garden</u> 4. M. T. Smith
Day Two
1. front 2. middle 3. front 4. back
Day Three
1. Chapter 1 **(Where Frogs Live)**
2. 6 3. Chapter 3 **(Types of Frogs)**
4. All About Frogs
Day Four
1. Front 2. Back 3. Middle 4. Back
Day Five
1. Taylor Dixon 2. <u>Our World</u>
3. <u>Soccer!</u> 4. Javier Ortiz
Review
1. Middle 2. Back 3. Front 4. Front

Week 31
Day One
1. cloudy 2. Wednesday
3. Friday 4. Rain
Day Two
1. red 2. 2 3. 9 4. yellow
Day Three
1. 4 2. beetles 3. 11 4. ants
Day Four
1. rain forest 2. eel
3. desert 4. anteater
Day Five
1. Friday 2. Wednesday
3. 7 4. Monday
Review
1. 4 2. kiwi 3. Yes 4. 10

Week 32
Day One
453 Oak Street
Trenton, NJ 55555
February 12, 2006
Dear Uncle Jim,
I am glad you came to see us! Your stories really made me laugh. Please come back soon.
Love,
Annie
Day Two
123 Main St.
Wichita, KS 55555
June 18, 2006
Dear Mrs. Jones,
I just read the book you wrote. It was great! I loved how Jesse solved his problems.
Sincerely,
Jack Morris
Day Three
14807 Lake Blvd.
Denver, CO 55555
Nov. 1, 2006

Dear Grandma,
Are you coming to our house for Thanksgiving this year? We're going to make your favorite pies! Please come.
Love always,
Cassie
Day Four
805 Duke Ave.
Austin, TX 55555
May 4, 2006
Dear Luke,
We are going camping this year for my birthday. I would like you to come with us. Do you think you can?
Your friend,
Jake
Day Five
Answers will vary.
Review
1400 Chalk Rd.
Spring, FL 55555
October 10, 2006
Dear **Aunt Maggie,**
Thanks for remembering my birthday. You know how much I like to read! The book is terrific!
Love,
Kevin

Month 8 Review
A. 1. The **(giant)** owl flew through the **(night)** sky. 2. It caught the **(scared) (little)** mouse.
B.
48 **River Road**
Memphis, TN 55555
June 18, 2006
Dear Uncle **Jay,**
I can't wait to go camping next month! I've already read **(Stars)** by Seymour Simon.
Love,
Andrea
C.
1. Gentoo 2. Emperor 3. Macaroni

Week 33
Day One
1. I found a <u>rock</u>. 2. It was in the <u>creek</u>. 3. The <u>stone</u> is flat.
4. The <u>water</u> made it smooth.
Day Two
1. Gray wolves <u>look</u> like big dogs.
2. They <u>live</u> in packs. 3. They <u>hunt</u> deer. 4. Some wolves <u>have</u> four pups.
Day Three
1. are 2. grow 3. is 4. has
Day Four
1. I 2. She 3. I 4. We

Day Five

One	More than One
child	girls
foot	men
tooth	mice

Review
1. Sofia and **I** have loose teeth.
2. Eric lost a **tooth** last year.
3. A new tooth **grew.**
4. I can't wait for **my** new tooth!

Week 34
Day One
1. Eric Carle writes books.
2. He wrote <u>The Very Hungry Caterpillar</u>. 3. I like to read <u>The Grouchy Ladybug</u>.

Day Two
1. <u>mother's day</u> is in May.
2. <u>earth day</u> is April 22.
3. Father's Day is always on <u>sunday</u>.
4. We love <u>valentine's day</u>!

Day Three
1. I live in the city of Mobile.
2. My state is Alabama.
3. The United States is my country.
4. I live in America.

Day Four
1. <u>willie mays</u> loved baseball.
2. He grew up in <u>birmingham, alabama</u>.
3. He played for the <u>new york</u> Giants.
 4. <u>mays</u> hit many home runs.

Day Five
1. I like spending <u>saturday</u> in the park.
2. We play softball there in <u>april</u>.
3. We watch butterflies in <u>june</u>.
4. Sometimes we go on <u>sunday</u> instead.

Review
1. **Alligators** live near water.
2. There are many alligators in **Florida.**
3. They build their nests in **June.**
4. **The** nests hold about 30 eggs.

Week 35
Day One
1. . 2. . 3. . 4. ?
Day Two
1. I saw <u>Dr.</u> Frost.
2. <u>Mr.</u> Lee is my teacher.
3. <u>Feb.</u> 28 is my birthday.
4. <u>Wed.</u> is the middle of the week.

Day Three
1. We buy fruit, vegetables, and bread.
2. I like science, art, and music.
3. Dogs, cats, hamsters, and fish make good pets.
4. Our garden is full of flowers, bushes, and weeds!

Day Four
1. December 31, 2000
2. Ogden, Utah
3. April 1, 1959
4. Chicago, Illinois

Day Five
1. A sea otter's fur keeps it warm.
2. Sea otters aren't quiet animals.
3. They're very playful.
4. Many otters live in California's oceans.

Review

> 125 Madrid Dr.
> Tucson, AZ 55555
> January 1, 2006

Dear Julia,
      The desert is fun in the winter. You should see the cactus here! Did you know that some are taller than me?
      Your friend,
      Anaya

Week 36
Day One
1. after 2. thank 3. how 4. going
Day Two
1. blue 2. bee 3. horse 4. one
Day Three
1. We sang a **tune.**
2. Can you **hop** on one foot?
3. **Clap** your hands!
4. The **hen** laid an egg.
Day Four
1. first 2. dirt 3. star 4. Sharks
Day Five
1. yellow 2. three 3. zoo 4. cold
Review
1. I **gave** him the ball.
2. I saw him **smile.**
3. Then he **said** good-bye.
5. I will **miss** him.

Month 9 Review
A. 1. **School** often starts in September. 2. **We** eat turkey at **Thanksgiving.** 3. **There** are **many** winter holidays. 4. **Do** you like to ski in the spring**?**
B. 1. Some dogs are trained to help <u>people</u>. **(N)**
2. Seeing-eye dogs <u>help</u> people who can't see. **(T)**
3. These <u>wonderful</u> dogs make life easier for many people. **(A)**
Why was the bug mixed up?
Because his uncle was an
(A) (N) (T) !
3   1   2